'I didn't expe
without love.

'I didn't expect yo...
caustically.

Melanie turned he...
She'd given herself out of love and there was no
shame in that.

She said with quiet defiance, 'I don't regret a
minute of it.'

'I don't regret it either,' he snapped, glaring at
her. 'I just wish there could have been more
between us.'

Dear Reader

The arrival of the Mills & Boon Mothers' Day Pack means that Spring is just around the corner ... so why not indulge in a little romantic Spring Fever, as you enjoy the four books specially chosen for you? Whether you received this Pack as a gift, or bought it for yourself, these stories will help you celebrate this very special time of year. So relax, put your feet up and allow our authors to entertain you!

The Editor

LEGEND OF LOVE

BY

MELINDA CROSS

MILLS & BOON LIMITED
ETON HOUSE   18-24 PARADISE ROAD
RICHMOND   SURREY   TW9 1SR

*First published in Great Britain 1992
by Mills & Boon Limited*

© Melinda Cross 1992

*Australian copyright 1992
Philippine copyright 1992
This edition 1992*

ISBN 0 263 77805 3

*Set in Times Roman 10½ on 12 pt.
91-9302-52709 C*

Made and printed in Great Britain

CHAPTER ONE

MELANIE ANNABELLE BROOKS stood at the window of Florida's Tallahassee airport, looking out at a small private jet that shimmered in the July heat waves rising from the tarmac even this early in the morning. She was a striking young woman who looked as out of place in the bland surroundings of the executive lounge as a tropical flower springing from the cement of a car park.

Long honey-blonde hair curved from a central parting to frame her face, then folded on her shoulders like the crest of a golden wave. She had the elegant features revered by a long-dead Southern aristocracy, and even motionless she seemed to exude that presence and bearing that only a life of privilege could impart. Her very stillness was somehow graceful, and there was a quiet elegance in her imperturbable blue-eyed gaze.

Had anyone looked beneath the composed exterior, beyond the carefully cultivated demeanour that often made her seem unapproachable, they might have detected a hint of sadness in the depths of those Southern sky eyes—a quiet longing so old and so vague that those close to her never saw it.

But no one looked that carefully at anyone, she was convinced; and that was part of the reason the world was such a lonely place.

She smiled at the morose turn her thoughts had taken and moved one shoulder, as if gloom were an unwanted passenger she could shrug off with a minimum of effort. There was no reason for such ponderous, depressing thoughts; not today. Today she would embark on an adventure, and, since she had never had one before, the prospect was exhilarating.

She'd dressed with even more care than usual, striving for a businesslike appearance with a sharply tailored, expensive white linen suit. Long, shapely legs tapered from beneath the skirt to soft white Italian pumps, and she carried a small matching leather clutch-bag in one hand.

There were several other people with her in the airport's executive lounge, but most were clustered around the bar in the rear, engaged in quiet conversation. For the moment she had the window, the view, and her thoughts to herself.

Her focus shifted slightly from the plane outside to her own reflection in the glass. She could barely make out the details of her face—a flawlessly beautiful face, everyone said, although Melanie often thought it just looked empty. At the moment her entire reflection was so bleached by the light from outside that she looked almost ghostlike.

Lately she'd begun to feel that way, too—like the sketch of a woman that hadn't been completed yet— and at those times she berated herself sternly for daring to feel the slightest discontent when life had been so good to her.

She closed her eyes briefly and forced herself to count her considerable blessings. With the single exception of her mother's death before Melanie's first birthday, every one of her twenty-four years had been the stuff of fairy-tales.

She'd been born to the wealth and rich tradition of a grand old Southern family, raised on a Georgia plantation by a doting father and a raft of loving servants, and last month, with a strange sort of helpless resignation, she'd finally become engaged to Beauregard Parker, a dashing Florida State congressman who'd been courting her extravagantly for over a year.

It even *sounds* like a fairy-tale, she thought with a trace of cynicism she couldn't seem to control, because in spite of all her blessings she was still troubled with the vague sense of something missing. Something important.

At times it seemed that her entire life had been preordained—as structured as the train ride from her home in Creek County, Georgia to the Tallahassee station. You got on at one end, and off at the other, and someone else had pre-scheduled all the stops in between.

Her engagement to a proper choice like Beau had been one of those fated stops, as expected of her as attending the right schools or maintaining a proper public decorum. Perhaps the sheer predictability of the event was what made her feel even more like merely a helpless passenger on the train of her own life.

Stop it, she scolded herself. Beau's a wonderful man, and there isn't a woman in the South who wouldn't give anything to be in your position. Besides, soon you'll be married, and then you'll have children, and surely children will banish that empty sense of something missing.

Or, she thought, tipping her head to one side, maybe it's as simple as a sense of purpose, and who knows? Maybe I'll find that on this trip.

She focused on the plane outside the window again, feeling a warming, pleasant flutter of pride that Beau had asked her, rather than one of his aides, to represent him on this congressional fact-finding tour. Almost as a reflex, she touched a lace hankie to the dampness in the hollow of her throat.

A tall man with the carefully manicured appearance of a magazine model stepped up to her side from the rear of the room, and she felt crowded all of a sudden, as if he'd trapped her against a wall.

'Uncomfortably warm, isn't it, darlin'?' Beau murmured close to her right ear. The slow, syrupy cadence of his drawl called to mind hot afternoons on the magnolia-scented porch of her Georgia home.

She looked up at him with a faint, automatic smile. 'A true Southern lady never feels the heat.'

'And you are nothin' if not a true Southern lady.' Beau's voice seemed to hum with pleasure, but his eyes betrayed his distraction by flicking repeatedly towards the lounge door as he watched for the arrival of the all-important Press. 'Did you read the society column this morning? They're calling Beauregard Parker's fiancée "the flower of Southern womanhood".'

Melanie winced at the time-worn label she didn't feel she deserved. It belonged to women of a different era: women who floated over marble floors in low-cut dresses with enormous hoop skirts—women like her own ancestral grandmother, whose sultry, distinctively Southern femininity seemed to sizzle from the old oil portrait that hung on Melanie's bedroom wall. 'There are no "flowers of Southern womanhood" any more, Beau.'

'Nonsense! Look at yourself.' He turned his head from the door long enough to beam at their dual reflection in the tinted glass. 'As a matter of fact, look at the both of us. I swear I don't know which one is prettier.'

She suppressed the giggle just in time. Giggling in public was unseemly behaviour, particularly for the fiancée of Florida's favourite young legislator. You could laugh quietly, demurely, and lord knew you could smile—you *had* to smile—but giggling was not permitted. Still, it was the one thing she had liked about Beau from the beginning—that, on occasion, he could actually make her want to laugh out loud.

'There's no contest, Beau.' Her drawl softened every word to a sultry lullaby. 'You're prettier by far.' She saw that famous million-dollar grin of his flash in the window, and wondered again if he had been elected for his political opinions or his looks. He had the tall, aristocratic bearing of old Southern gentry, softly waved brown hair, and hazel eyes that brightened when he turned on the charm. The trouble was, she could never quite tell when the charm was genuine, or merely expedient.

'You *are* beautiful, Mellie,' he whispered, his breath stirring her hair. 'I'm the envy of every man who sees you...' Someone from the back of the room called his name and his eyes darted away from her like two startled birds. 'Excuse me, darlin'. I'll be right back.'

She nodded absently, looking back at her reflection, imagining she saw in the glass not a faint image of herself, but of the woman she'd idolised since childhood; the woman whose portrait hung over her bed. Like that woman, she had a rosebud mouth, whose corners lifted now as she recalled the day she'd rescued the painting from the attic, nearly twenty years before.

It had been a gloomy Saturday in her fifth year, with a steady rain polishing the fat, glossy leaves of the eucalyptus trees that lined the drive. The family's antebellum mansion had been a vast, lonely place for an only child; but the warm, cavernous attic, cluttered with the memorabilia of generations, was a strangely comforting haven. Being surrounded by the carefully stored possessions of all the Brookses who had gone before had given Melanie a much-needed sense of family continuity—an important feeling for a motherless youngster.

She'd found the portrait jammed behind boxes in a dusty corner, and had immediately dragged her new-found treasure downstairs to show her father.

'By heaven, I never knew this was up there, Mellie,' he'd said with a quirky smile. 'Do you know who this woman was? She was my great-great-grandmother. You were named after her, honey.'

'I have that beautiful lady's name?'

'You do indeed. And her looks, too, I think.' He'd propped the painting up against a wall and backed away, shaking his head with a little smile. 'They say she was a bit of a black sheep, you know. Her own husband crossed her name out of the family Bible, although I never was told why...'

'What's a black sheep, Papa?'

He'd sighed with a helpless kind of fondness, then scooped her up in his arms. 'Just someone who's a little different, Mellie.'

'Will I be a black sheep like her?'

'Oh, my, no,' he'd laughed. 'You're going to be my perfect little Southern lady, aren't you, Mellie? Just as your mother was.'

But she hadn't grown up to look like the fading photographs of that gentle, acquiescent soul who had been her mother—she looked like the first Melanie Annabelle Brooks—the family's black sheep.

The air seemed to push against her as Beau breezed up to her side again, and she wondered if this was what it would always be like—Beau rushing in and out of her life and her thoughts like a fickle wind.

'Well, Mellie, it's almost time. Are you excited about your little trip?'

'Yes.' This time her smile was genuine. 'Thank you for trusting me with an assignment like this, Beau. It means a lot to me.'

He chuckled quietly. 'Don't get yourself too worked up, darlin'. It's not as if I'm sendin' you to negotiate world peace. It's just a goodwill trip, the kind of thing politicians' wives do all the time. And, since that's what you're going to be in another few months, I thought this might be good practice.'

Melanie's brow threatened to crease. 'You make it sound unimportant.'

'Why, Mellie!' He turned her gently by the shoulders to face him and looked down at her with a wounded expression. 'Of course it's not unimportant! Would I have chartered that jet if it were unimportant? Would I have called a Press conference if it were unimportant?'

His expression was so boyishly earnest that Melanie's lips twitched with amusement. 'You'd call a Press conference to announce the weather if you could get away with it,' she teased gently. 'You're a

politician down to your bones, Beau Parker, and don't
you try pretending you're not.'

Strong white teeth flashed sheepishly in the sun-
bronzed face. 'Guilty. But there's more to this
goodwill jaunt than meets the eye, Mellie, and I'm
countin' on you. Don't think I'm not. Benjamin Cage
is a power to be reckoned with in this state, and when
he sends an invitation any politician who wants to stay
a politician sends a representative.'

Melanie sighed again, basically indifferent to the
convoluted workings of politics. It was confusing,
tiresome, and somehow a little distasteful. 'It doesn't
seem right, Beau, that one little businessman should
have that kind of power...'

'He's a *big* businessman, darlin',' he corrected her.
'Half the country drinks orange juice from his groves
every morning, and ever since he heard the Florida
legislature intended to cut some of the funding for
the Everglades, he's been plastering "Save the
Everglades" all over every bottle and carton. Now if
we were to ignore his little invitation to see what's
happening down there first-hand he might just decide
to use all that advertising against us...understand?'

Melanie made a little face. Beau might think this
was all legitimate politics, but it sounded like
blackmail to her. 'So how many other congressmen
are sending representatives on this junket?'

Beau shrugged. 'Who knows how many he invited?
But I imagine you'll be a veritable parade, tourin'
Cage's little Everglades.'

'*His* Everglades?'

'The way he talks, you'd think it was his.'

Melanie's brow arched in disapproval. The
Everglades comprised millions of acres of sawgrass

plain and dark, watery mangrove forests—the entire southern section of Florida. Anyone who thought of land that vast as his own private property was too arrogant for her tastes.

'I'm not going to like this man,' she stated with conviction.

Beau chuckled at her expression. 'I don't doubt that for a moment, darlin'. You and Mr Cage are on opposite ends of the social scale, I'm afraid. Clawed his way to the top, from what I hear, and doesn't think much of anyone who didn't have to do the same thing.'

Melanie's nose wrinkled. She'd encountered prejudice against those born to wealth before, and in her opinion it was just as insensitive as prejudice against those born to poverty. If you were going to judge people at all, you should judge them by what they did with their lives, not the circumstances of their birth. Benjamin Cage was sounding more unlikeable by the minute.

'He's a loner, too,' Beau went on. 'No family, no social life to speak of—doesn't seem to care much for anything or anybody, except that big swamp, and you can't talk reason to the man about that. If he had his way he'd pump every tax dollar the state raised into the place. I suppose he's hoping a private tour will convince the lawmakers that the Everglades needs more money next year, not less.'

Melanie nodded soberly; professionally, she thought. 'I'll listen to everything he says, Beau, and I'll take meticulous notes. By the time I get back you'll have all the information you need to cast an informed vote.'

Beau chuckled and shook his head a little, his eyes darting back to the door before meeting hers. 'Darlin',

I already know how I'm goin' to vote. My advisers don't think pouring money into a swamp makes much sense, and, frankly, neither do I.'

Melanie blinked at him, stunned. 'You've already decided how to vote?'

He nodded distractedly.

'But . . . then why are you sending me down there?'

'Because, Mellie,' he said, a trace of impatience creeping into his voice, 'I wouldn't want Mr Cage tellin' the voters I'd made a decision without hearin' all sides of the issue first, now, would I?'

'But, Beau . . . isn't that just what you're doing . . . ?'

'Now, now,' he interrupted her. 'Don't you worry your pretty little head about it, darlin'. It's just politics. All you have to do is go on down there and look interested when Cage takes you all on his tour, and maybe use some of that Southern charm on the man so it won't sting so much when I vote against him.'

For a moment, all Melanie could do was stare at him in disbelief. The disappointment would come later. '*That's* why you're sending me on this trip instead of one of your aides?' she finally asked in a whisper. 'Because I'm more charming than some near-sighted clerk in a three-piece suit?'

His mouth twitched in an uncertain smile, then his eyes jerked with obvious relief to the sudden flurry of activity behind them. 'Oh, dear. Looks as if the Press is going to interrupt us again. Sorry, Mellie, but I'm afraid this will have to wait.' He gave her waist a quick squeeze, then turned to face his public with a brilliant smile that didn't look sorry at all.

Melanie was too well-bred, too well-trained for her destined role as this gentleman's lady to make a scene in front of the journalists and photographers who quickly surrounded them.

After a full ten minutes of questions and photos, Beau held up one hand with an apologetic gesture. 'I'm sorry, ladies, gentlemen, but that's all we have time for this morning...'

'How about a goodbye kiss for the front page, Congressman?' a reporter called out, grinning.

'I trust you're suggestin' I kiss this beautiful creature, and not you, sir,' Beau fired back with his own grin, eliciting hearty laughter. 'And in that case, I'm most happy to oblige.'

Melanie submitted to one of the dry, passionless kisses Beau always gave her in front of the cameras, wincing inwardly because it seemed so contrived. It was at moments like these that she felt more like a stage prop than the professed love of his life.

'That wasn't the way I wanted to kiss you,' he whispered in her ear, almost as if he'd sensed her disappointment, 'but the way I wanted to kiss you was absolutely not for the public eye.'

She stilled in his arms for a moment, struck by the thought that, pristine as the kiss had been, it wasn't really all that different from the ones they shared privately. He just breathed harder when they were alone, that was all. She leaned back in the circle of his arms and gazed up at him, and, although that was the loving picture that ultimately made the front page of the Tallahassee paper, the photographer didn't see that her smile was a little strained.

Less than an hour later her small jet touched down at a private airstrip near Florida's Gulf Coast, just a few miles north of where the land designated as the Everglades began. She got off the moment the metal

staircase unfolded from the door, relieved to be off
the plane where she had been the only passenger.

The airport itself was little more than a few metal
hangars clustered around a single-storey brick building
with a short tower. She was walking briskly towards
the double glass doors in that building when a deep-
throated shout stopped her.

'Hey! You!'

She turned and squinted against the glare of sunlight reflecting off one of the metal hangars. When
her eyes adjusted she saw the distant figure of a man
standing perfectly erect next to an open Jeep.

'Where's the congressman?' the man shouted, and
Melanie's brows arched slightly in disbelief. Surely this
couldn't be the driver sent to fetch her to her hotel?
In *that* vehicle? Even from this distance she could see
the battered, mud-covered fenders and the ominous-
looking rollbar.

'Are you addressing me?' she asked without raising
her voice, refusing to bellow across an airfield like a
common barker.

It surprised her a little that the man heard her at
all; surprised her more when he began to cover the
distance between them with impossibly long strides.

As he drew closer her first thought was that he must
be a military man, his posture was so erect, his gait
so measured. The thought faltered a bit as she noticed
the very unmilitary clothing—heavy canvas trousers
tucked sloppily into knee-high boots, and a mud-
coloured sleeveless T-shirt that left tanned, muscular
shoulders and arms bare. Any notion of a military
connection collapsed entirely when he got close
enough for her to see his face; the face of a man she

knew instinctively would never take orders from another.

He stopped directly in front of her. 'Yes, I'm "addressing" you.' His voice had the same powerful resonance at a conversational level as it had in a shout. Melanie blinked, as if the force of it had blown across her face like a strong wind. 'So where's the congressman? I take it that *is* his plane?'

Melanie nodded stupidly, mesmerised by one of the most exotic-looking men she had ever seen. His hair was swept straight back from a high brow, its colour so purely black that even under the morning sun there were no highlights; just an even, blinding gleam. His face was deeply bronzed and almost ageless, it was so free of character lines. There was a faint, lighter-coloured webbing at the corner of each eye that marked prolonged squinting in the sun, but, other than that, the face gave no hint that any emotion had ever found expression there. His nose was strong and straight, his cheekbones high and proud, his mouth wide and crisply carved. Brows as black as his hair made two slashes over equally black eyes. The general impression was one of fierce indomitability, and only fascination kept Melanie from turning instinctively and running the other way.

'So?' he asked impatiently.

'Um . . . I beg your pardon?'

'So, if that's the congressman's plane, where is he?'

'Oh.' She licked her lips, unaccountably nervous. 'He isn't coming. I'm his representative——'

'*What*?'

Melanie took a quick step backward. 'I said I'm Congressman Parker's rep——'

'I *heard* what you said, I just can't believe it!' He spoke in the rapid, clipped speech of a northerner, making his verbal attack sound all the more vicious. 'Parker isn't coming himself? He sent . . . *you*?'

It was his contemptuous emphasis on the word 'you' that finally succeeded in snapping Melanie out of her trance. Her back straightened, her chin lifted, and those Southern sky eyes sparked with indignation. 'Yes, if it's any of your business,' her voice crackled with the haughtiness only a Southern drawl could produce, 'he sent *me*. Now, if you'll stand aside, I'll go inside and connect with my driver . . .'

'You have connected with your driver,' he snapped. 'I'm Benjamin Cage.'

Melanie's eyes swept over him once with thinly veiled disbelief. *This* was Benjamin Cage? A man so powerful that his invitations couldn't be ignored, even by legislators? 'You can't be,' she said without thinking how foolish it would sound.

His face was stone, only a slight narrowing of the black eyes revealing any life at all. 'Who the hell are you?' he demanded.

She tried to match his emotionless stare with one of her own, but it was hard to manage with her head tipped back to look up into his face. Besides, if this really was Benjamin Cage, she was supposed to be charming him, not alienating him. She adjusted her tone accordingly. 'Congressman Parker is very interested in what you have to say about the State budget for the Everglades, Mr Cage, but it just wasn't possible for him to get away right now. That's why he sent me.'

Cage arched one brow, but said nothing.

'Please be assured that I'll convey everything you say to the congressman, and he'll consider it carefully before the vote on the budget next month...'

Her voice trailed away under his hard stare, and she swallowed. Clearly he was furious that Beau hadn't come himself, and if Beau's political future really depended on this man, he was in trouble indeed. 'The legislature *is* in special session, Mr Cage. I'm sure none of the other congressmen could get away to come in person, either,' she finished lamely.

Cage stared at her for a moment longer, then turned his head and looked off into the distance. 'I didn't invite any other congressmen.'

A careful upbringing kept Melanie's mouth from falling open in surprise. No one else was coming? No great crowd of people to ask informed questions, to occupy Cage's attention so she could fade into the background?

He turned his head to look down at her, his eyes hooded. 'Your Congressman Parker is the one legislator really pushing for a budget cut. I thought if I had a chance to show him how disastrous that would be for the Everglades, he'd convince the rest of them.' He sighed and one corner of his mouth tightened. 'The plan was to have his undivided attention for a few days so I could show him—one-on-one, man-to-man—the way things were down here.'

Melanie hesitated for a moment. 'You can show me. I'll tell him,' she said quietly, meaning it. Beau might not have sent her here to bring back information, but that didn't mean she couldn't do it anyway.

His chest and shoulders moved in what might have been a silent laugh. 'And who's to say he'll listen to you?'

She made no response at all for a moment, almost wishing he'd get angry enough to send her back to Tallahassee. Damn Beau for letting her think she was being sent on a real fact-finding mission; damn him for weaving her into this net of half-truths, making her an unwilling participant in political manoeuvrings she couldn't begin to understand; and damn him in particular for placing his future in her hands, knowing that her loyalty, once given, was a point of honour she couldn't betray.

'He'll listen to me,' she finally said with more conviction than she felt, forcing herself to meet Cage's intrusive stare. When she did, she felt that sudden vacuum inside she associated with the downward plunge of a roller-coaster.

He studied her face for such a long time that she became uncomfortable, then his lips tightened. 'I guess I don't have much choice but to take you at your word, do I?' He looked off to one side and sighed, and she caught a glimpse of a profile that looked as if it had been carved from granite. 'All right. We might as well get started. Let's get your luggage in the Jeep.'

She waited until he'd turned his back before taking a deep, quiet breath of relief. All things considered, she thought she'd done very well so far, walking that fine line between loyalty to Beau and her own sense of right and wrong. Without lying, she'd managed to weather Cage's anger that Beau hadn't come himself; she'd convinced him she was an acceptable envoy... and, she reminded herself wryly, watching his long strides eat up the tarmac as he walked towards the Jeep, you've talked yourself right into three days alone in the world's biggest swamp with a man who wears sleeveless T-shirts and rubber boots.

She caught her breath at that, feeling a strange quiver she finally recognised as a sense of impending adventure. Part of her wished she were back in Tallahassee—but, with her eyes on Cage's broad back, another part wasn't wishing that at all.

CHAPTER TWO

MELANIE had ridden in a convertible once, back in college when she'd been Queen of the Magnolia Parade. Riding in Benjamin Cage's open Jeep was nothing like that.

From the smooth tarmac of the airfield, he turned on to a narrow dirt track with rocks the size of a man's fist jutting out of the packed sand, and that was when the fun began. Her heart in her throat, her right hand clutching the armrest in a white-knuckled grip, Melanie repeatedly bounced high off the passenger-seat in wide-eyed, terrified silence. Only her shoulder harness kept her inside the vehicle, and only the fear of biting off her tongue kept her from shouting at Cage to slow down.

I should have worn a hat, she told herself as they sped down the track through an open sawgrass plain. It was not yet noon, but already intolerably hot, and Melanie felt like a helpless titbit in an open skillet, sizzling under the merciless gaze of the Florida sun. Between the bone-jarring bumps that seemed to jam her spine up into her brain, she worried about sunburning her face, then chided herself for worrying about such a little thing when she'd never survive the Jeep ride anyway.

'It's not the best road,' Cage hollered over the noise of the straining engine, and if she'd been able to open her mouth against the hot wind of their passage she would have laughed out loud at the understatement.

22

She risked a hasty sidelong glance at Cage's profile, and could have sworn she'd just missed seeing a wicked smile. Damn him, he was actually enjoying her discomfort, probably punishing her because she wasn't Beau.

After what seemed like an interminable ride through the open space of the sawgrass plain, the little car shot suddenly into a hole in a thick, seemingly impenetrable stand of enormous hardwoods. Melanie squeezed her eyes shut and prepared for the inevitable collision, never for a moment doubting the victor in a battle between one of the monstrous trees and the tiny car. A short time later the Jeep slammed to a halt, flinging her forward against the strap of her harness. She kept her eyes closed for a moment, listening to the tick of the cooling engine, stunned to realise none of her bones were broken.

'You bastard!' she wanted to shriek at Cage, but Southern ladies of Melanie's standing did not shriek, nor did they stoop to guttural name-calling. She satisfied herself by turning her head slowly and giving him one of her most contemptuous, haughty glares.

He had his head tipped towards her expectantly, waiting for her reaction. With some dismay she noted that, even expressionless, his face conveyed more pride, more haughtiness than hers could ever muster with a conscious effort of will.

'Next time,' she told him with a voice that would have melted butter and burned it black, 'I'll drive.'

The mechanics of Benjamin Cage's reluctant smile were fascinating to watch. The wide, sharply chiselled mouth elongated slightly as muscles contracted on only one side, as if smiling was too painful an expression to commit fully. 'Here we are,' he said shortly, turning to face front, his mouth working to control the smile.

Melanie squinted through the mud-splattered windscreen, then frowned. For all practical purposes, they were in the middle of a towering jungle, parked in front of a small house perched precariously on a number of stilts. 'Where, exactly, is here?'

'Home,' he replied, those black eyes fixed on the pathetic structure rising from the forest floor. 'Well, not home, exactly; more like a weekend cabin. I come here when I need to get away from everything else.'

Melanie eyed the deeply shaded tangle of jungle that pressed in from all sides, making the already small house appear even smaller. 'Really,' she said with forced politeness, wondering why on earth anyone would choose to spend time in the ominous shadow of such an alien landscape. 'You mean you actually stay here?'

'As often as I can, for as long as I can. It's about as far as I can get from the office.'

Her smile was small and tight. 'Well, I'm sure it's very nice.'

This time he did laugh out loud. 'I'm glad you think so, since it's where you'll be staying, too.'

Obviously it was a joke; another sadistic attempt to get a rise out of her, just like the wild Jeep ride. 'Indeed.' She tossed out the word with a light chuckle, refusing to give him the satisfaction of appearing *that* gullible. He couldn't possibly expect her to stay in a place like this...

'Of course, you'll have to leave your modesty at the front door. The place is too small to provide much privacy, and I wasn't counting on having a woman guest.'

Slowly, lips parted incredulously, Melanie turned and looked at him. 'You're not serious. You expect me to stay *here*?'

'Of course I'm serious. You've got to live in the Everglades to understand them, even if it's only for a few days. The motels are for tourists. You want to be Congressman Parker's representative? You want to see what I intended to show him? Then this is how we start.'

A weak, breathy laugh escaped her lips as she looked at the house, seeing it differently now that she knew she was expected to live in it. Was it actually teetering on those stilts? Didn't the stilts themselves look more like toothpicks than the massive beams they actually were? Her concentration on the house was so intent that she barely noticed when Cage got out of the Jeep and started hauling her luggage up the dozen rickety steps that climbed from the forest floor to a wrap-around screen porch.

'Coming?' he called down from the top step.

Frozen in her seat, she looked up, up, at where he towered above her like some primitive god on his wilderness throne. She took a long time fumbling with her shoulder harness, suddenly reluctant to leave the uncomfortable, terrifying Jeep, now that she'd seen the alternative.

She wouldn't stay here, of course. She couldn't. Even if she managed to climb those splintered steps in her slender heels; even if her extra weight didn't snap the stilts and send the house crashing to the ground; there was still propriety to be considered. Young Southern ladies didn't spend unchaperoned weekends alone in the wilderness with strange men; especially not when those young ladies were engaged

to up-and-coming congressmen constantly in the
public eye. But how to refuse graciously, without offending the man Beau thought so important to his
political future?

She had to concentrate to keep her brow from fur-
rowing as she worked her way through the dilemma.
For all Cage's stoic demeanour, she'd sensed a certain
pride in this awful place, like a young boy eagerly
showing off a tree-house he'd built himself. Wounding
that pride with an out-of-hand rejection certainly
wouldn't do Beau any good. The least she could do
was climb up and look at the place, and if she didn't
kill herself on the steps he'd see the foolishness of the
plan for himself once she got up there. It was perfectly preposterous, imagining that any lady could be
housed in such surroundings.

She took a deep breath and stepped from the Jeep,
trying to ignore the way her expensive heels sank into
the soft silt. She hesitated at the bottom of the stairs.
There was no railing.

'I can come down and carry you up, if you like.'

He was taunting her, or challenging her—she wasn't
sure which. 'Thank you, no. I can manage.' She placed
a foot on the bottom riser and the step, little more
than a slab of hewn wood, sagged under her weight
and she froze.

'You sure?'

Melanie swallowed. 'Quite sure.' She waited until
she heard the screen door slam above her before continuing her terrified, stiff-legged climb.

Only when she reached the safety of the top landing
did she release the breath she'd been holding and smile
tremulously, inordinately proud of her accomplish-
ment.

'Congratulations,' he said from the other side of
the screen door, and Melanie bristled at the mockery
in his tone. She stood rigid and quietly furious, glaring
at him through the distortions of the screen, wondering how long it was going to take this Bohemian
to open the door for a lady. She went immediately
slack-jawed when he ignored her, turning to walk
deeper into the dimness of the cabin. 'Come on in,'
he called over his shoulder.

'You *could* open the door,' she snapped.

'So could you.'

She made an audible sound of exasperated disapproval, then jerked the door open, stepped inside, and
let it slam shut behind her.

The entire cabin was a single square room. In size,
it was close to the small formal parlour of Melanie's
childhood home, but any similarity ended there.

'How . . . rustic,' she said, for lack of a better word.
'Rustic' seemed far too generous. Every visible
surface—walls, floor, angled ceiling—was made of
splintery, bare wood, with mud-coloured caulking
filling in the chinks and spaces.

Large openings in three of the four walls opened
directly on to the screened porch to catch the slightest
breeze. Above each a fitted piece of plywood was
hooked to the ceiling, and Melanie shuddered, imagining how ominously dark the place would look with
those shutters down and latched against the weather.
A rough-hewn slab of lumber stretched the full length
of the fourth wall, serving, she imagined, as a counter-
top of sorts. There was a single bed in a far corner,
a small wicker sofa and chair in the room's centre.

'Sit down,' he told her as he bent to drag a large cooler from beneath the makeshift counter. 'I'll get us something to drink.'

Melanie walked gingerly to the only chair and sat down on the vinyl cushion, making a crinkly sound. She sat with her back straight and her bag clutched in her lap, like a woman who wasn't planning to stay long. She caught herself watching as his brown, muscular arms wrestled with the heavy cooler, then looked down, a little embarrassed.

'Oh,' she said quietly, noticing the woven mat beneath her feet for the first time. It covered a large area of the floor, its bright blues and reds and yellows the only colour in an otherwise drab space. 'This is beautiful. Where did you get it?'

'Not far from here,' he replied, telling her nothing. The floor creaked as he walked over to sit on the sofa that faced her. He passed her one of two small glass bottles dripping condensation.

'Wine cooler?' she asked, covering her distaste for the carbonated wine so prevalent in the marketplace these days.

'Worse. It's a bottled rum drink. A little rum, a lot of fruit juices. Totally offensive.'

Suppressing the urge to ask for a glass, at least, Melanie took the bottle, relishing the sensation of anything cold and wet in her palm. 'Why do you drink it, if it's so offensive?'

He almost smiled. 'I meant it would be totally offensive to you. I kind of like it, myself. But then, I'm easy to please.'

'Implying that I'm not?' she asked, a little testily.

'Implying that, from the looks of you, I'd guess you were more the champagne type.'

While she was trying to decide whether that was a compliment or an insult she sipped from the bottle and was surprised to find the drink quite palatable. She took another sip, then licked her lips. 'Actually, it's very refreshing. I think I like it.'

'It's almost a hundred degrees out there, and you haven't had anything to drink since the plane. You'd probably drink beer out of a barrel and love it at this point.'

Melanie's eyes widened slightly at the crude image, and thought she saw him start to smile again.

'You should change clothes right away. You must be sweltering in that get-up.'

She plucked self-consciously at the front of her suit jacket, pulling it away from her body to let some air circulate. 'I'm quite comfortable for the time being, thank you. I can wait to change until I get to my...'

'Maybe I didn't make myself clear before. If you're really going to take Congressman Parker's place for this weekend you're going to see the Everglades the way I planned to show it to him. From here. No motel, or no tour, take your pick.'

Melanie hesitated, wondering which would be worse as far as Beau was concerned: going back to Tallahassee now, alienating Cage and thus failing in her assignment; or staying alone with him in this God-forsaken place...

'Well? What's it going to be? I have a schedule too, you know. It wasn't easy to carve out these three days. I'd like to know they aren't going to be wasted.' He was leaning forward on the sofa now, his bare arms braced on his thighs, nearly empty bottle dangling between his knees. His black eyes never left her face.

She cleared her throat and swallowed. 'Surely you can see the impossibility of the situation,' she said in her most cajoling, honeyed drawl. 'You said yourself you never expected a woman guest, and you obviously don't have the accommodation...'

'You can have the bed. I've got a sleeping-bag.' The short clip of his northern accent made his words sound more sensible than hers; more definite. 'Don't worry. I have no intention of raping you during the night.'

Only the startled look in her eyes conveyed her loss of composure. 'The thought never crossed my mind,' she said stiffly.

'Is that a fact?'

Melanie didn't know if he was mocking her, or trying to frighten her, but in either case a haughty glare seemed an appropriate response. 'I'm concerned about the lack of privacy, and the lack of propriety in staying here, Mr Cage—not whether or not you will behave like a gentleman.'

'Who told you I was a gentleman?'

She hesitated for an instant, caught off guard by the question. 'I was giving you the benefit of the doubt,' she said frostily. 'Perhaps that was a mistake.'

His laugh filled the cabin. 'Giving any man the benefit of the doubt is always a mistake for a woman who looks like you,' he smiled, and Melanie thought she had never seen such a wicked smile in her life. 'However, in deference to your obvious naïveté, I promise I'll try to behave like a gentleman for the duration of your visit.' His smile tilted a bit. 'I'm not promising I'll succeed in my efforts, you understand.'

Melanie narrowed her eyes at the thinly veiled threat, and finally decided that it had no substance. He was still trying to intimidate her, and he'd almost succeeded simply by saying things he knew perfectly well would shock a lady. The truth was, she was the one who had *him* over a barrel. If he really wanted his information on the Everglades to go back to Beau he was going to have to play by her rules, not the other way around. Finally she spoke with all the dignity she could muster. 'Your promise isn't necessary, Mr Cage, since I have no intention of staying here. I'll stay at a hotel, or I won't stay at all.'

She watched with satisfaction as one of his black brows shot upward. She wondered if anyone had ever said no to him before.

'All right,' he finally said with a little shrug. 'Have it your way.'

She tempered her victory with one of her loveliest smiles. 'You'll see, Mr Cage. Spending my nights at a motel won't at all limit what I can learn when we go touring during the day...' Her sentence trailed away as he stood abruptly, picked up her bags from beside the bed and walked to the door.

'Come on. I'll drive you back to the airfield.'

'The airfield? But I thought...'

Her bags hit the floor with a double thump and he turned to face her chair, his back ramrod-straight, his chin high, only his eyes looking down. Melanie felt as if she was growing smaller under his stare.

'I told you,' he said flatly, 'I made time for this weekend because I knew actually living in the 'Glades would show Congressman Parker the need for more State funding. A lot of what happens here happens after dark, and you don't see much of that from an air-conditioned motel-room. So, if a motel is your condition for staying, then staying is pointless.' He picked up the bags again and moved towards the door.

'Now just a minute!' Her call stopped him, but now that she had him stopped she didn't quite know what to do with him. She looked down at her bag, still clutched tightly in one hand, as if that piece of very expensive leather could somehow solve her problem. Perhaps it was time to try a different tack.

'I confess I don't know what to do. I'm not sure which would be worse: abandoning my assignment, or my better judgement.'

'Are the two mutually exclusive?'

She looked up at him, big blue eyes troubled. 'I don't know,' she said in absolute honestly. 'It would help if I could call Beau...'

'Beau?'

She nodded. 'Congressman Parker.'

He snorted derisively. 'How did you ever land a job as a congressional aide without being able to make decisions on your own?'

Her eyes flickered. 'You don't understand. I'm not his aide. If that's all I were I wouldn't have to worry so much about how my behaviour would reflect on his...'

'Wait a minute. What do you mean, you're not his aide? What are you, then?'

She collected herself, straightening in the chair. 'I'm his fiancée, of course; the closest personal representative he could send. That's why you can be sure that I'll relay whatever I learn here directly back...'

The bags hit the floor again, startling her into silence. She didn't like the way he was looking at her. For once there was open expression in the black eyes, and Melanie decided immediately that she'd liked it better when they were unreadable. As it was now, they were narrowed and strangely bright for all their dark colour, focused on her with a fury so evident that it was almost palpable. He muttered a violent oath under his breath, and she wisely decided now would not be the time to criticise his language. 'You're his *fiancée*? He sent his *fiancée* on a fact-finding tour? What the hell did he think qualified you to investigate something this important? That you're good in bed?'

Melanie's jaw dropped open. 'How *dare* you say such a thing to me . . .?'

'And how dare *you* try to pass yourself off as a qualified professional when all you really are is——?'

'I *didn't*!' The unintentional volume of her own voice astounded her. Oh, lord, what was happening to her? Melanie Annabelle Brooks, daughter of the South, a well-bred lady of refined sensibilities, and here she was, bellowing like a hog-caller.

Mortified, she closed her eyes briefly, then forced the music of quiet modulation into her voice. 'I did *not* try to pass myself off as any such thing. I said I was representing the congressman, and that's precisely what he sent me down here to do. He had the perfectly silly idea that I would be one of several representatives on this tour; that sending someone as close to him as I am . . . might tell you just how much importance he placed on this trip . . .' Her voice faltered, then faded at the uncomfortable memory of why Beau had really sent her down here.

Cage's eyes narrowed in contempt. 'Is that what he told you?' She looked up sharply, but couldn't meet his cold, hard stare. 'You know exactly why he sent you down here, don't you?' he demanded. 'You're the decoy; the ''representative'' that's supposed to convince me and the Press that he's willing to listen to both sides of the issue. But he has no intention of really listening, does he?'

Melanie felt slightly ill to hear Beau's motives stated so plainly. The deception had made her uncomfortable when she'd first learned about it at the airport; now she felt somehow soiled to be a part of it. 'I think . . . I think you're making an unjustified assumption . . .'

'Are you a liar, too?'

Her eyes flashed a more brilliant blue at the personal attack. 'No!' she sprang to her own defence automatically. Beau might have made her an unwitting partner in deception, but she wouldn't lie outright for him. And yet if you continue this deception for Beau's sake, she thought miserably, a liar is exactly what you'll be. 'I am not a liar,' she mumbled, slumping a little in the chair.

There was silence for a moment as she stared vacantly at the far wall, trying to sort through the muddle of her thoughts. 'Come on,' she heard him say at last, and it was the gentleness of his tone that disturbed her more than anything else. All of a sudden he was trying to be nice to her; maybe, heaven forbid, because he pitied her for being as much a helpless pawn in this situation as he was. His contempt would have been preferable. 'I'll take you back to the airfield, Miss . . . what the hell is your name, anyway?'

'Melanie,' she replied tonelessly. She was still staring at the wall. 'Melanie Annabelle Brooks.'

He grunted softly, almost as if someone had punched him gently in the stomach. 'Melanie *Annabelle* Brooks?' he repeated softly. 'From Creek County, Georgia?'

She nodded absently, used to people recognising her name. Lord knew it had been in the society columns enough lately.

'Good lord,' he murmured after a moment of stunned silence. 'Full circle. It comes full circle...'

Puzzled, she looked up and frowned at him. He was staring out through the screen, and there was something wild about the way the light from outside limned his profile, outlining the strong nose, the firm jaw, the slight jut of his chin. 'Melanie Annabelle Brooks...' He repeated her name tonelessly, like a litany. 'Maybe it's true after all, what the Indians say... that the destiny of the adult is written in the name of the child.' He turned his head slowly to look at her. 'That grand names mandate grand deeds.'

Melanie looked away, a little uncomfortable with her notoriety. Just because her family's name had been in the social register for generations, it didn't mean there were grand deeds written in her future. If she had a destiny at all, it was to take her proper place in society as the devoted wife of some fine Southern gentleman. That had been the role of all the Brooks women throughout history.

Still staring at the wall, she wondered what it would be like to have a greater purpose; to leave a mark on history more memorable than an oil portrait gathering dust in a forgotten corner of an attic. 'Mr Cage,' she said suddenly, struggling with a vague, barely formed thought she couldn't quite articulate yet, 'what if... what if I was to stay...?'

'It's pointless. We both know that. Why continue the charade?'

She frowned and pursed her lips, then turned abruptly to look at him. 'Perhaps it did begin as a charade, Mr Cage; but it doesn't have to end as one.' The only outward sign of her anxiety was her hand's tightening on the purse in her lap. 'Aside from the reports Beau gave me to read, I don't know a thing about the Everglades. Frankly, I don't know much beyond the front veranda of the Georgia plantation where I grew up. But I'm not entirely without influence on Beau, and if you can convince me voting for the cut in the budget is a mistake . . . maybe I can convince him.'

The offer was genuine, but in the circumstances it sounded feeble, even to her. Cage thought she'd been in on the deception from the beginning; that she'd always known the trip was a sham; so why should he trust her now? She watched his face, but there was no change in his flat, oddly emotionless gaze, and she had already resigned herself to the angry refusal she deserved when he said, 'All right.'

She blinked once, so startled by the reply that she didn't know what to say.

'We'll give it a try.'

Her lips moved involuntarily into a tremulous smile, and she caught herself wondering why on earth she was suddenly so happy that he had agreed to let her stay.

For a long moment, only the ratcheting sound of insects from outside broke the silence. Finally the floor beneath Cage squeaked as he shifted his weight and looked down at her, those black eyes narrowed in the bronzed face, fixed so intently on hers that she felt almost physically violated. 'The first thing we have to do is get you out of those ridiculous clothes . . .' he let the words hang for a moment, enjoying her re-

action, then added '...into something cooler. You
have a lot to see, and it's hot where we're going.'

Melanie smiled with nervous relief, unobtrusively
pulling her jacket away from her damp skin. 'And it
isn't here?' she asked wryly, rising from her chair and
smoothing the wrinkles from her skirt as she looked
around. 'I'll just wash first, if you don't mind...'
The sentence trailed away into the hot silence of
midday. 'Where's the bathroom, Mr Cage?' she asked
after a moment.

He was smiling when she looked at him. 'What
bathroom?'

CHAPTER THREE

NO BATHROOM. The words loomed ridiculously large in Melanie's mind, blocking out all other thoughts. She'd already forgotten about the impropriety of spending three days alone in this Everglades cabin with Benjamin Cage. Such a minor thing paled in the shadow of that short, yet overwhelming phrase—no bathroom. She quelled the impulse to sink back down into her chair and instead turned to face Cage directly.

He was still standing by the door to the porch, his head turned slightly towards her, those black eyes watching, waiting for a reaction. He probably thought she was a spoiled, simpering fool—a woman totally incapable of living outside her own sheltered, pampered environment, even for three days. And he wasn't far from wrong. She'd balked at staying in this place even before she'd learned there was no bathroom...

'No running water,' he interrupted the silence. 'No electricity, either.' His eyes swept over her expensive suit and shoes, as if to emphasise the obvious point that she did not belong here. She clenched her jaw, thinking that he was doing this on purpose: goading her into leaving just because that was what he expected her to do.

A tiny seed of rebellion flickered to life deep inside. All her life she'd done what people had expected of her—men, in particular. For her father first, and then for Beau, she'd always been precisely what she'd been born and raised to be: perfectly mannered, perfectly

38

feminine—perfectly predictable. Both men would be horrified to think of her in conditions such as these, and suddenly that had a strange sort of appeal.

'If there's no bathroom where I can wash,' she tried to force nonchalance into her voice, 'I suppose you'd better show me the alternative if I'm going to stay here.' She felt a peculiar, racing thrill when one of his brows arched. She'd never taken a man by surprise before, and surprising this particular man was eminently satisfying.

That brief flare of bravado dimmed rapidly as she followed him down the steps outside, eyes and ears tuned to the surroundings with a new, very personal interest.

After the noise of the Jeep, the forest had seemed deadly silent when they'd first arrived, but now a veritable cacophony of sounds assaulted her ears from the wet, brilliantly green world that surrounded the cabin. Unseen insects buzzed and chirped and whirred; birds squawked and warbled and even screeched as they soared over the canopy above them.

On the ground every frond of every fern seemed to quiver, as if with the passage of a large, invisible beast, and the spongy humus gave way beneath the points of her heels with little sucking sounds as they circled the stilted house. She followed Cage closely, trying to plant her feet in the large prints left by his boots.

'That's the outhouse.' He stopped and pointed to a small half-wood, half-screened structure set back into the trees.

Melanie nodded silently, imagining a thousand scurrying creatures chasing her down that narrow path in the dark of night.

'And over here is the shower.'

'The shower?' She followed him around the thick timbers that supported the right corner of the cabin, her eyes hopeful. They clouded with dismay when he picked up the spray nozzle of a hose that snaked downward from a small hole in the porch floor above.

'There's a barrel up there that collects rainwater. Open this nozzle——' he pushed the trigger and a brief spray of water emerged '—and you have a hand-held shower.'

Melanie pursed her lips and looked around worriedly. 'But . . . it's right out in the open. There aren't any walls . . . not even a curtain . . .'

'You won't need one.' He gestured at the seemingly impenetrable greenery surrounding them. 'The forest may have a thousand eyes, but none of them is human.'

She smiled thinly at that, finding it very small comfort; and then she thought how odd it was that he hadn't considered she might have been worried about *his* eyes.

In the dry, almost lecturing tone of a bored tour guide he continued to explain the archaic water system. 'We're in the middle of the wet season now, so water conservation isn't quite so critical, but we still have to be careful. Never, ever leave the hose open, or you'll drain all the drinking water. If all you need is a quick wash, for instance, just fill that basin over there.'

She followed his gaze, then blinked in stupefied disbelief. The 'basin' was a shallow depression chipped into a waist-high tree stump.

'Clever,' she mumbled, but 'primitive' was the word that first came to mind. Primitive, uncivilised, barbaric. From the corner of her eye she saw the glint of light on metal and looked up. 'What are those?' She pointed at the broad, saucer-like rings of metal circling each of the stilts halfway between the ground and the cabin floor above.

He followed her gaze and shrugged. 'They help keep some of the wildlife out of the cabin. The rodents can't climb over them, and the snakes don't like to. The edges are very sharp.'

Melanie literally felt the blood draining from her face. 'Snakes?' she said in a small voice. 'In the cabin?' She had an immediate vision of snakes writhing over her in bed, and for a moment thought she might prove that irritating old caricature of faint-hearted Southern belles by swooning dead away.

'Don't worry about it. Most of them are harmless anyway.'

'Really,' she smiled weakly. 'How reassuring.'

'Come on back upstairs. I'll show you how to get drinking water out of the barrel, how to run the oil lamps, and then you really should change into something cooler. You look a little pale.'

He thinks I look pale now, she thought numbly as she followed him back up the steps. Wait till he sees me after I've met my first snake.

She traipsed behind obediently as he showed her where things were in the cabin, but she only pretended interest, reasoning that he would always be here to do whatever needed done. While he showed her how to light the smelly oil lamps and trim the wicks so they wouldn't smoke, her mind wandered back to her pampered youth on the family plantation in Georgia. Whenever the power went out during a storm, the servants had always moved through the house like candle-lit wraiths, carrying oil lamps with crystal teardrops that tinkled when they moved. She drifted with the memory, feeling oddly sleepy. She barely noticed when Cage stopped talking and narrowed his eyes at her.

'You're not paying attention,' he said sharply.

She started a bit, then focused on the unusual prominence of his high cheekbones, mostly because she didn't want to meet his eyes. It seemed exceedingly hot and close all of a sudden, and she touched the dampness in the hollow of her throat with her fingers. When she blinked it was all she could do to open her eyes again. Her lashes felt heavy and wet. 'Do you think I could have a glass of water?' she asked, her voice breathy and shallow. 'It's very warm, isn't it?'

Without warning he reached out to lay both hands on her cheeks. Normally she would have jerked back from such familiarity, but her reactions seemed abnormally slow, as if she were trying to move through air that had suddenly become syrup.

'Damn,' he spat, scowling down at her. 'I should have known. That fair skin, those blue eyes . . .'

Her head wobbled a little to one side and she blinked at him stupidly. His face seemed to swim in and out of focus, and oddly the blurring made some things more clear—like his eyes. They weren't really black; the brown was just so dark that it looked as if they were. And they weren't cold, unfeeling eyes, either. As a matter of fact, they looked positively hot, like two dark points of fire burning in his face . . .

'I think . . .' she started to say, blinking hard to clear her vision, wondering what was wrong with her. Was this strange, disconnected wooziness the way people felt when they were going to faint? 'I think I'm a little dizzy...' Her knees buckled abruptly and Cage grabbed her quickly by the upper arms.

Oh, look at that, Melanie thought, blinking up at him. Look at the pucker between his brows; look at how worried he is about me. Isn't that nice?

'Easy...' She heard him speak, but it sounded as if he were very far away. 'Easy, now.' He spoke again, and his voice was beautifully deep, like the distant rumble of the night train she'd heard as a child from her bedroom window. It was a pleasant, soothing sound, and yet a haunting one, making her long for places she'd never seen; things she'd never done...

'Here. Let me help you.' She felt his arm snug around her waist, supporting her so that her feet barely touched the ground, and then somehow she was in the chair and he was bent over her, his hands pressed against her cheeks, his eyes worriedly searching hers. His hands felt rough, and very hot.

'Dammit,' he muttered. 'I'll be right back. Don't move.'

She almost giggled at the order, it was so foolishly unnecessary. Her legs were rubber, and even if they could have supported her weight, her thoughts were too fuzzy to engineer the movement.

He was back almost before she knew he was gone, pressing a glass of cool water to her lips, a damp cloth to her forehead. It was the most delicious water she'd ever tasted, and she would have drained the glass if he hadn't taken it away. When she looked up to ask for more he shook his head before she could give voice to the request. 'Not just yet.'

'I'm still thirsty...'

'I know you are. You can have more in a minute. Are you feeling better?'

'Yes, I'm feeling better...' She looked down as he knelt in front of her chair and watched the deft movements of his hands as they unbuttoned her jacket. There was something wrong about his doing that, but whatever it was kept slipping away in the fog of her thoughts. Besides, the air felt deliciously cool against the skin of her chest.

She watched his face as he parted the jacket, pressing the damp cloth to the sides of her neck, and then to the hot flesh that rose above the lace of her bra. There was a strange tightness around his eyes and mouth, as if he was exerting great effort, and she wondered what could be so hard about holding a little washcloth to her chest. After a moment she shivered involuntarily, and Cage took the cloth away and stood up.

'Here.' He handed her the glass of water and she drank again. Her focus on the world seemed to sharpen a little, and she looked up at him. What she saw in his eyes made her cheeks redden and her hands fly to pull her jacket closed. His only response was a tight smile.

'Thank you. That's much better,' she said, a little too fast. 'The room isn't spinning any more. That must be magic water.'

His lips twitched a little. 'Any water is magic when you're courting heatstroke. That was too close a call. You mustn't have had much to drink on the plane...'

'I didn't have anything to drink on the plane.'

He frowned at her. 'When did you drink last?'

'You know...that rum thing you gave me...'

'Don't remind me. I mean before that.'

She frowned, trying to remember. 'Early this morning, I guess. I had orange juice for breakfast. Some of your orange juice, as a matter of fact.'

'Breakfast? That must have been hours ago. What're you trying to do? Kill yourself? You're fair-haired, fair-skinned—you should know that makes you twice as susceptible to heatstroke.'

'That's ridiculous.' She fluttered her hand impatiently. 'I've never, ever suffered from heatstroke, and I've lived in the South all my life...'

'Unless I miss my guess, you've lived in air-conditioning all your life.'

'So?' she grumbled, thinking of the vast air-conditioned spaces of the family mansion, the pleasantly shivery chill of the Tallahassee hotel-room she'd stayed in last night.

'So you don't know the first thing about staying healthy in this kind of heat and humidity,' he snapped. 'If you did, you would never have accepted alcohol when you were already thirsty. Nothing dehydrates you faster.'

Her mouth twitched petulantly. 'You gave it to me...'

'I know I did! I also gave you credit for having a little common sense!' He closed his eyes briefly and blew out a long, exasperated sigh; then dropped to a crouch at the side of her chair, putting his head directly on a level with hers.

'Listen, Ms Brooks. If you're really going to stay here, and I emphasise the word "if", you're going to have to learn some new rules very fast.'

Melanie looked into the depths of eyes that made her want to look away and eyes that made it impossible to look away, all at the same time. She

frowned and tried to sound decisive. 'There's no "if"
about it. I told you I would stay, and that's what I
intend to do.'

'Only if I let you.' His eyes were fixed on hers, just
inches away.

'You need me, remember? I'm the only chance you
have to convince Beau to change his vote. You have
to let me stay.' Her smile was just a little smug, and
Melanie decided she was feeling much better indeed.

'I don't have to do anything.'

Her smile faltered, then faded entirely.

He was very close. So close that the sheen of his
black hair was almost blinding; so close that his eyes
seemed like dark doorways she could walk through
into rooms she'd never seen before. She caught herself
breathing deeply, discerning for the first time in her
life the scent of another human being. His was sharply
aromatic, like the floor of a pine forest after a rain.
Did Beau have a scent? she wondered, and then
realised immediately that he didn't. Not one of his
own, anyway.

'But I want to stay,' she whispered, wondering why
it was suddenly so important to her.

He regarded her steadily. 'Will you follow the rules
I lay down? No questions, no arguments?'

'Yes.' The breath from her mouth stirred the short,
fine strands of hair at his temple.

His eyes were still fastened on hers, but she couldn't
read them. 'You'll have to drink a lot of fluids, even
when you don't think you're thirsty—at least twice as
much as I drink. Agreed?'

She nodded.

'No heavy exercise, no big meals, just lots of small
ones, and wear a hat outside all the time . . . you did

bring a sun hat, didn't you?' She shook her head and
his mouth tightened impatiently. 'Never mind. We'll
get you one. How about clothes? What do you have
in that bag?'

'Another suit, a sundress, a cocktail dress...'

'A *cocktail* dress?' He straightened instantly to his
full height and scowled down at her. 'You brought a
cocktail dress for a tour of the Everglades?'

Melanie's eyes flashed at his tone. 'I thought I was
going to be staying at a hotel!' she snapped up at him,
her chin jutting defiantly. 'A hotel with a lounge and
a restaurant and air-conditioning and maybe even
running water!'

Even through her anger she had the sense that he
was about to burst out laughing, and then she wondered where she had ever got such an idea. His stony
expression hadn't altered a fraction. 'All right,' he
said quietly, handing her the glass, watching her drink
the rest of the water. 'I guess the first order of business
is a shopping trip to Everglades City. We're not going
into the 'Glades until we get you dressed decently.'

She arched one brow at his use of the word 'we',
but made no comment. Wondering if staying here with
this man was the biggest mistake of her life, or if she
had even bigger ones to look forward to, she took his
hand and let him help her from the chair.

'Still a little shaky?'

She wasn't, but she liked the feeling of his arm
firmly circling her waist. A lady should always be able
to count on the support of a man. That was the way
it was meant to be. 'Yes. Just a little.'

CHAPTER FOUR

EVERGLADES CITY was a seemingly endless drive from Benjamin Cage's isolated cabin. The roads were tortuous, rocky paths when they could be called roads at all, and Melanie was certain all her joints had been dislocated by the time Cage finally pulled the Jeep on to a smoothly tarred surface that promised civilisation just ahead.

'City' was a misnomer for the one-traffic-light Florida town whose main attraction was its Gulf Coast entrance to Everglades National Park. A few tourists wandered the main street, and as the Jeep slowed Melanie looked at their brief shorts and loose T-shirts with envy. Her linen suit had lost its crispness and its bright white colour long ago, and, aside from feeling unkempt and wilted in the heat, she felt ridiculously overdressed.

Cage pulled into the shady car park of a drive-in restaurant and turned to speak briefly into the speaker. Melanie stared at the back of his head, fascinated by the unrelieved blackness of his hair, wondering what ancestor had donated that particular recessive gene.

Suddenly he turned towards her and she caught her breath at the overpowering masculinity of his face. 'Hungry?' he asked her.

She brushed nervously at the long tangles of windblown blonde, tucking them behind her ears. 'Not a bit.'

'Nevertheless, you're going to eat.'

She nodded without protest and he raised his brows. 'You're very good at taking orders, aren't you?'

'That was the agreement, wasn't it? You lay down the rules, I follow them.'

His brows lowered back to their original position. 'Yes, that was the agreement. I just didn't expect it to be this easy. Somehow I pegged you as the kind who'd fight me every step of the way.'

Melanie's laugh was cultured—cultivated, actually—as musical as wind chimes in a soft breeze. 'I've never been the kind of fool who balks at doing what's best for me, Mr Cage.'

He was silent for what seemed like a long time. 'So you always do what other people tell you is best for you?' he asked quietly.

She thought about that for a moment, searching her memory for a single instance of even minor rebellion, but finding none. What had there been to rebel against? Why would she ever have questioned the guidance of people like her father, like Beau, who had only her best interests at heart?

Besides, there was a certain security in always being told how to behave, what to wear, what schools to attend and what young men to date. You never made any mistakes that way.

Cage was still looking at her, waiting for an answer, but before she could reply a young waitress in shorts and a halter top brought a tray of covered dishes and fastened it to his door. Melanie couldn't help but notice the way the girl's heavily made-up eyes sparked when they saw Cage's face. She flashed him a brilliant smile as she pocketed a generous tip, then looked over her shapely shoulder twice as she walked away.

Brazen, Melanie thought. 'Do women always react to you that way?' she asked archly.

Cage cocked a brow in puzzlement. 'What way?' He looked after the waitress with the expression of a man who thought he might have missed something.

Melanie's lips flattened a little. 'Surely you're not going to tell me you didn't notice that.'

'Notice what?'

'Her reaction to you, of course,' she said a little more snidely than she'd meant to. 'For heaven's sake, she did everything but crawl into the car...'

His sudden smile was open, almost boyish, and Melanie couldn't decide if it was genuine or contrived. 'Really? How nice.' He looked over at where the young waitress was leaning on a serving counter that opened to the inside kitchen, her weight on one leg, the opposite hip cocked and straining against the brief shorts. 'I didn't notice,' he mused. 'Maybe you could give me an insider's insight on the nuances of female behaviour...' This time when he looked back at her there was a definite twinkle of amusement in those black eyes. Melanie scowled at him.

'Here.' He passed over a tall glass of some kind of juice and an oblong dish heavy with an assortment of freshly cut fruit and a small loaf of crisp bread. 'Eat it all.'

The tart-sweet aromas of cantaloupe, water-melon, pineapple, mango, grapes and a few other fruits Melanie didn't recognise assailed her nostrils. Suddenly she was ravenous. 'I couldn't possibly eat this much,' she said automatically, but within moments she'd proved herself a liar. Her dish was nearly empty by the time she realised Cage was watching her. She glanced up at him, then down at her plate, embarrassed. 'I must have been hungrier than I realised,' she mumbled.

'They say the enjoyment of food is a measure of sensuality.'

Melanie almost choked on the last piece of pineapple. She coughed, then swallowed. Even without looking she knew he was wearing that expression that looked as if it wanted to be a smile. 'Where to next?' she asked, still staring down at her plate.

'First to get you some decent clothes, then back to the cabin. Are you finished with that?'

She passed him her totally empty dish with a sheepish expression, appalled by her own bad manners. Ladies always left a few morsels on their plates, indicating a dainty, controlled appetite. She closed her eyes as Cage started the Jeep and pulled out of the car park, thinking that she'd only been away from her own environment for a few hours, and already she was shedding the lessons of her twenty-four years of gentility.

He bypassed the main street's stores and drove to a rather shabby shop on one of the back lanes. 'This is Hildy's,' he explained as they entered the door to the chiming of a little bell. 'The locals get almost everything they need right here. Main Street is for the tourists.'

Melanie looked around the small interior, so crammed with merchandise that there was barely room to walk sideways down the aisles. The predominant smell was rubber, and the predominant colour was a mud green.

Cage walked straight to a table of jumbled knee-high boots and started rummaging. 'Here we go.' He held a pair of sickly brown rubber ones aloft. 'These are about your size. Try them on.'

She eyed the cumbersome things sceptically. 'I really don't think they'll be necessary . . .'

'We'll be doing a lot of walking through wetlands.' He looked straight at her when she didn't move to take the boots. 'Snake country,' he added softly.

Melanie tried on the boots.

Within five minutes Cage had managed to select the most unattractive assortment of clothing Melanie had ever seen in her life. There were baggy canvas trousers, similar to what he wore; two long-sleeved shirts in the same muddy green colour; two T-shirts, a pair of tennis shoes, some walking shorts, and the boots, of course. He dumped it all on the check-out counter next to the cash register, then went back for a broad-brimmed straw hat.

'Perfect,' Melanie muttered, staring at the tacky hat with its attached black scarf, wondering what she'd look like with it tied under her chin.

Cage snapped the folds out of one of the shirts. 'Here. Turn around and we'll see if this is too big.'

She sighed and turned, arms outstretched while he held the shirt up to her shoulders.

He gazed critically at the fit at the shoulders, then his eyes dropped to the generous swell of her breasts and froze. Melanie caught her breath silently when she saw him swallow. His eyes lifted slowly to meet hers. 'We'll just check the length of the sleeves,' he murmured, his lips barely moving. Melanie lowered her arms and felt the cuffs of the sleeves brush against her fingertips. His hands still held the shirt at her shoulders; his eyes still stared into hers. 'How is it?' His words ran together in a quick exhale.

'Fine,' she whispered, transfixed by his eyes.

Mindlessly his thumbs moved downward, drifting lightly over the lapels of her jacket just above the rise of her breasts. Melanie's eyes widened at the sensation of the jacket's silk lining being pressed against her skin. She saw the sudden tightening of the flesh at the corners of Cage's mouth, and without realising it responded by letting her head fall backwards ever so slightly. The movement was too imperceptible to be measured in anything but increased heartbeats.

The soft sound of the shirt crumpling to the floor made them both start. For a moment they stared at each other wide-eyed, like guilty children, then Cage ducked abruptly to retrieve the shirt.

Melanie blinked her way out of what had seemed like a dream, amazed to find him behaving as if nothing had happened. What was he doing, bent over the counter like that, scribbling on that tablet? And what had happened between them just a moment ago, and why wasn't he affected by it? 'What are you doing?' Her voice sounded husky.

His pencil froze for a moment, then he cleared his throat and started writing again. 'Listing everything we bought and the price.' *His* voice was normal; crisp, cool, distant.

Melanie licked her lips. Nothing had happened. He'd held up a shirt and it had dropped to the floor, that was all. Anything else had been simply the product of her imagination. She frowned hard and looked down at the scuffed wooden floor. 'Shouldn't we wait for someone . . .?'

'Hildy'll put it on my bill. She's probably out fishing.'

'Fishing?' It pleased her that the huskiness in her voice had disappeared, and she looked up. 'She went fishing and left the store wide open?'

He signed his name with a flourish and straightened. 'Hildy fishes every day, and she always leaves the store open in case someone needs something. It's a small town. Here. You carry these.'

He handed her the boots, looked at her thoughtfully for a moment, then took them back. 'There's a bathroom in the back,' he said with a half-smile, handing her some of the clothes and the tennis shoes, 'the last real one you'll see in a while. Why don't you take advantage of it while I take the rest of this out to the Jeep?'

He was halfway to the door before the blush reached Melanie's face.

While barely large enough to turn around in, the bathroom was infinitely preferable to the outhouse she'd seen at the cabin, and Melanie savoured the small luxury. With a scrap of soap on the ancient, pedestal sink she gave herself a cursory sponge bath before donning the new clothes, then brushed her hair back to its honey-blonde perfection and repaired her make-up.

Five minutes later she walked back out to the Jeep, carrying what felt like her identity in her arms. Her slip and tights were neatly hidden within the folds of the suit she carried on her arms; her expensive pumps dangled from two fingers.

She wore a black T-shirt and, over that, one of the muddy green shirts she'd left unbuttoned. The stiff canvas trousers were rolled halfway up her calves so she wouldn't trip on the too-long legs, and the blindingly white new tennis shoes were surprisingly comfortable.

To her own eyes she looked ridiculous in the too-large clothes, but she knew that some men found that lost-waif look strangely appealing. She wondered what Cage would say.

He gave her a cursory glance as she crawled into the Jeep, but made no comment on her appearance. 'Ready?' he asked simply, and, when she nodded, he pulled away from the kerb with a short squeal of the tyres.

On the bone-jarring ride back to the cabin, Melanie caught herself scowling more than once, miffed that Cage hadn't said something—*anything*—about the way she looked. In a way, she had always depended on the comments of the men in her life as a barometer of her own appearance, and hearing no comment at all on such a marked change made her un-comfortable. Not that she needed constant compli-menting, of course; she was just used to being noticed. Beau would have noticed. Beau would have taken one look at this outrageous outfit, chuckled in that throaty way of his, then told her she looked irresistible, like a little girl playing at dressing up. But then again, she thought snippily, Beau was a gentleman well-versed in the proper way to treat a lady.

If anything, the cabin looked worse on second sight.

'Take your things upstairs and put on your boots,' Cage told her perfunctorily when he'd turned off the engine. She was almost halfway up the steps when he added from below, 'And take off that bra while you're at it. You'll be hot enough without wearing more than you have to.'

Blushing furiously, she hurried up the rest of the stairs without looking back.

So. Cursory glance or not, he'd noticed a good deal more than she'd thought. A good deal more than he should have, she amended, her mouth twitching angrily once she was inside the cabin. How dared he make such a suggestion? And if he thought she was going to follow it, whatever his reasons, he had another think coming.

She was bent over the bed, laying her suit out, when Cage's voice came from behind her, making her jump. 'Do you have something to tie back your hair?' He hadn't made a sound coming up the steps or into the cabin, and that he could move so quietly frightened her. He was standing in the doorway watching her, the light from behind making it impossible to distinguish his features.

'A clip, somewhere,' she replied, a little breathless from surprise. She knelt to the floor and started rummaging through her case. 'Here it is.'

'Good. Pin it up, then put on your hat. I'll spray you downstairs.'

She frowned as she caught her hair on top of her head with the clip, then looked back over her shoulder. The doorway was already empty, as if he'd never been there.

After pulling on the tall, hot boots and snatching her new hat from the bed, she stomped down the steps to where he waited at the bottom.

He held a spray can of insect repellant in one hand like a weapon. 'Put on your hat, then close your eyes,' he ordered. She did as she was told, shivering when the cold spray hit the skin of her hands and neck, wrinkling her nose at the awful smell. When he was finished she backed away from the chemical cloud and coughed.

'That's disgusting,' she complained.

'Agreed. But you'll need it. The biting flies and mosquitoes around here have fantasies about fair-skinned blondes like you.'

She cocked her head and eyed his bare head and arms. 'Why do I have to wear a hat and a long-sleeved shirt when you don't?' she grumbled.

He snorted softly, then simply turned away without answering, making her feel stupid for asking in the first place.

'Come on,' he said over his shoulder, crossing the small cleared space around the cabin in just a few steps. Melanie caught her breath when he seemed to disappear into the wall of green, then hurried after him while the movement of ferns and leaves still marked his passage.

The greenery that had seemed solid was merely a narrow circle of underbrush around the cabin. Once on the other side, walking was easy between the monstrous oaks and mahogany trees whose leafy tops formed a canopy that blocked out the sky and kept the forest floor relatively free from undergrowth.

It was dim, cool, and surprisingly quiet in this cathedral-like stand of giants, and the ground felt firm and dry beneath Melanie's boots. Just when she was beginning to wonder why she'd had to wear them at all, her right foot sank into a small, sucking bog of mud. Cage stopped and turned back to look at her when she emitted a small sound of surprise.

'It's going to get a whole lot worse,' he warned her. 'We're coming to the end of this hammock. We'll be wading soon.'

Melanie swatted at a persistent mosquito less offended by the insect spray than she was. 'What's a hammock?'

Cage smiled. 'An island of trees in a sea of water. That's what the Everglades is, basically. A million tiny islands in a vast sea.'

After walking a few more moments, they emerged with startling suddenness from the dark forest into the full light of the sun. Melanie squinted as her eyes adjusted, then breathed a soft 'oh' at the sight.

For almost as far as she could see an ocean of tall grass swayed in the gentle current of the unseen water at its base. Sunlight sparkled off the lighter tips of the tall sawgrass like millions of pin-point fireworks, entrancing the unwary. Mesmerised, Melanie took a few steps past Cage and promptly sank in water almost up to the tops of her boots. Before she could even open her mouth to cry out in surprise, she felt herself lifted by the waist and swung back to relatively dry ground.

Cage's face was expressionless when she looked up at him, but he kept his hands firmly on her waist. 'Beside me, maybe,' he said. 'Behind me, preferably; but never, ever walk ahead of me again.'

Blue eyes wide, as startled by the pressure of his hands as she had been by the sudden plunge into the water, she nodded without saying anything.

'I'm beginning to think you should be on a leash.'

She narrowed her eyes and twisted free of his hands, placing her own on her hips as if that would erase the memory of his touch. 'I'm quite capable of following a few simple guide-lines,' she snapped, 'if you'd just be responsible enough to lay them out for me.'

He stared at her so intently that she had to concentrate not to drop her eyes. 'Fair enough,' he said finally, looking off into the distance. 'You've already learned your most valuable lesson: there's water everywhere. In dry-down, during the northern winter, you can walk across this plain; but now, in the rainy season, most of the 'Glades is under water, even when it looks dry.'

'The River of Grass,' she murmured a description she'd read, following his eyes across the vast, unbroken stretch of sawgrass.

'Exactly. And if you don't know where to walk, follow in the footsteps of someone who does, or don't move at all. Otherwise you're going to get wet.'

Melanie sighed, then nodded. 'So how do we cross?'

'The same way you'd cross any stretch of water. We float.' He turned right and walked along the edge of the hammock, never checking to see if Melanie was following precisely in his footsteps, as ordered. She was, of course, but it would have been reassuring to know he was keeping an eye on her.

She stumbled along behind for what seemed like a long time, watching the careful placement of her feet, glancing up only occasionally at the broad muscles of his back moving beneath the thin cotton jersey of his T-shirt.

It pleased her to notice the fabric clinging damply to the indentation of his spine, just as her own shirt was. Somehow knowing that at least his body reacted to the heat and humidity made him seem more human.

There wasn't a breath of wind, and moving through the sauna-like air was like trying to walk through soggy cotton. After five minutes Melanie was breathing through her mouth and her boots felt like concrete blocks weighing her down. 'Where are we going?' she asked, plucking her shirt away from her breasts, angry because her bra was chafing her skin.

'We're there,' he announced, stopping suddenly.

When Melanie looked past him she saw a small lagoon biting into the island of trees. At its apex was a short wooden pier, incongruous in this wilderness of plants. More incongruous yet was the strange-looking craft tied to a mooring post.

'Oh, my,' Melanie murmured, recognising the odd shape of the common Everglades airboat. They were little more than platforms with huge fans twice the diameter of a man's height fastened on the back. She'd seen them on television, whizzing through shallow water at breakneck speeds, passengers strapped help-lessly to the chairs screwed into the deck, looking horribly exposed.

'Have you ever ridden on one of these?'

Melanie shook her head weakly, shuffling as he took her hand and pulled her out on to the dock, and then on to the airboat's platform. It rocked beneath their weight and Melanie spread her legs and locked her knees to keep her balance.

'You'll sit here, in the front,' Cage said, whisking a canvas cover from a chair fastened close to the front edge of the boat. With her peripheral vision Melanie noticed a sudden movement from the chair seat that made even Cage jump backwards into her. She cried out and would have fallen overboard if he hadn't spun in place, grabbed her arms and jerked her full-length against him. She froze in his arms, her fingers wrapped reflexively around his biceps, her heart thundering against his chest. She didn't breathe for a moment, her mind racing to process the sudden input of sensory data.

Surely she was imagining his hands moving on her back, pulling her almost imperceptibly closer; surely it was a sudden breeze and not his breath stirring the wisps of hair on her forehead beneath the brim of her hat. And of course there was no fire in those black eyes as they gazed down at her—it was only a reflection of the sun bouncing up from the water.

She caught in a quick breath at last, and as her lungs filled her breasts swelled and pressed against his chest. She felt him stiffen against her, then his brows twitched in a hard frown.

'Nothing to worry about.' His voice rasped like the low notes on a cello. 'We just startled it, that's all.'

'Startled what?' she whispered in confusion, following his gaze to the chair where she was supposed to sit. She went instantly rigid and her eyes snapped wide as she watched a long, mud-brown snake uncoil, slither down from the seat, then across the platform to slip silently into the water. 'Omigod,' she whispered, and then her knees gave way and she sagged against him.

'I thought I told you to take off that bra,' was the last thing she heard before blacking out.

CHAPTER FIVE

MUFFLED sounds lapped at the door of Melanie's consciousness—the sporadic rasp of a single insect; the muted caw of a distant bird; the gentle sigh of grass blades rubbing against one another. As if sounds had opened the door to all her other senses, she suddenly felt the heat and weight of the humid air; the insidious brightness of sunlight spearing through her closed eyelids. Her eyes fluttered open, squinted against the light, and finally focused on the strong planes and angles of Cage's face suspended above her. Good lord. She was lying in the man's lap.

'What happened?' she mumbled, scrambling to sit up.

'Apparently you don't like snakes,' he said, tucking his legs into a lotus position, his torso swaying slightly with the gentle motion of the airboat.

Melanie's eyes shot to the chair seat, then darted wildly around the platform.

'It's gone,' he reassured her, 'and it was harmless anyway. A simple banded water snake. Looks a lot like a water moccasin, but it's not poisonous. You didn't have to worry.'

Melanie suppressed the urge to giggle hysterically. She hadn't fainted because she'd thought the snake was poisonous; she'd fainted because it was a snake. Period. 'I hate snakes,' she shuddered.

62

He made a derisive sound of exasperation. 'Then what the hell are you doing in the Everglades? The place is full of them.'

'I'm not here to make pets out of the wildlife,' she defended herself hotly. 'I ought to be able to learn something about this place without sharing my chairs with reptiles.'

He looked at her for a moment, then turned and looked off across the waving sawgrass sea. Melanie studied the proud lines of his profile etched against the field of tall grass, and felt the anger slowly seep out of her. There was an inexplicable sadness in the way he stared off into the distance; something tragic that seemed to tremble just beneath the surface of his seemingly impervious face.

'I promise not to faint any more,' she said softly, not really understanding what had prompted her to say it.

He looked at her with mild surprise, as if he'd forgotten her presence entirely until she spoke. His lips compressed briefly, as if irritated at the reminder. 'What are you doing here?' he asked abruptly. 'How did Parker talk you into coming?'

Melanie frowned down at her lap, remembering how proud she'd been when Beau had first asked her to represent him on this trip...back when she'd still thought the trip had meaning.

'He didn't have to talk me into coming,' she said quietly. 'I wanted to. I thought I'd be doing something important, something worthwhile.'

He sighed noisily. 'And when did he tell you the truth?'

'This morning,' she mumbled. 'At the airport, just before I left.' She shrank from the emptiness of his stare, knowing what he was thinking. Getting on that plane after she knew about the deception made her part of it. 'The Press was there,' she added hurriedly, trying to defend her actions. 'I didn't want to make a scene...' She stammered to a halt, uncomfortable under his gaze. 'He's my *fiancé*,' she insisted, as if that would explain everything.

'Does that title carry a requirement that you agree with everything he does?'

Melanie bit down on her lower lip. 'Of course not. But questioning him in public would have been inexcusable. Especially about his political judgement. I don't know a thing about politics...'

'You don't have to know anything about politics to know what's right.'

'Knowing what's right and having the courage to act on that conviction are two very different things, Mr Cage. There are no rebels in the Brooks family.'

For a moment he looked at her as if she'd said something incredibly stupid, but then he turned away quickly, and Melanie wasn't sure she'd seen the expression at all.

'Let's get going,' he said gruffly. 'You have a lot to see, and three days isn't much time.'

She nodded and stood up, taking a wide stance to counter the slight movement of the deck beneath her feet.

'Strap yourself into the front chair,' he directed. 'This afternoon we'll take a short tour of the immediate area, just to give you the lie of the land.'

With ill-disguised nervousness, Melanie settled herself in the chair towards the front of the platform, tightened the lap belt, then grasped the armrests so tightly that her knuckles whitened. Cage slipped the casting ropes from cleats on the dock, then climbed up on to the pilot's platform that perched high above the main deck, directly behind Melanie. She watched over her shoulder as he checked gauges she couldn't see, then suddenly he looked down at her. She faced front quickly, feeling like a student caught staring at the teacher.

'We won't be able to talk much over the noise of the engine,' he said from behind her. 'But after we cross this stretch of sawgrass there's a slough where the alligators congregate. We'll stop the boat there so we can talk.'

Melanie's eyes widened at the mention of alligators, and her mouth opened to rattle off a series of questions. Did alligators eat people? Could they climb up on the boat? Could the boat tip over? The engine roared to deafening life before she could ask a single one, and the initial thrust forward pushed her back against her seat.

After a few moments—long enough for Melanie to decide that Cage was a capable pilot and the boat was more stable than it appeared—fear gave way reluctantly to fascination. She watched the river of grass flatten beneath their passage, then with childlike delight saw it spring upright behind them, as if they'd never been there. The hot wind was a blessed relief against her face, and Melanie lifted her head and let the funny straw hat slip down her back to hang by the scarf tails.

For a time it seemed that the sawgrass stretched to the horizon, that the distant clumps of trees were miles and miles away. But then suddenly the grass opened on to a corridor of deeper black water banked on either side with water-lilies; then just as suddenly the

sawgrass disappeared entirely behind thick brush that
crowded the water on both sides.

Cage throttled back the engine to a soft rumble,
and they puttered down the watery aisle at walking
speed while Melanie looked around with wonder. She
laughed aloud when their passage disturbed a flock
of odd, spindly-legged wading birds, sending them
skywards, with a graceful rush that belied their ungainly appearance. The Everglades wasn't so bad, she
was thinking. It wasn't the dark, sinister jungle she'd
imagined, with monstrous reptiles jumping out at you
from dank pools of stagnant water. It was open and
light and golden in the sun, with lush, exotic plants
and snowy birds that beat their wings against an
endless expanse of blue sky.

And then suddenly it all changed. The boat followed an abrupt twist in the watery path, and it narrowed rapidly as the surrounding greenery seemed to
close in, robbing the world of light.

They passed another flock of wading birds off to
the side, smaller than the first, with rosy patches
brightening their white plumage. 'Roseate spoon-
bills,' Cage informed her. Big wings flapped diffi-
dently as the airboat passed their fishing hole, but
they didn't take flight. When he cut the engine abruptly the sudden silence was eerie.

'We'll let the current take us from here,' he said
quietly from behind her. 'This is the slough I told you
about. Keep your eyes open, and you'll see a lot of
the local residents. Like there.' He pointed to a sandy,
lumpy cove set into the right bank, open to the sun.

'Where?' Melanie whispered, leaning in the direction he was pointing with a puzzled frown, looking
for wildlife but seeing none. Her eyes widened when

one of the well-camouflaged lumps opened jaws as long as her arm, exposing a row of sharp, pointed teeth that seemed to glitter in the sunlight. With a slow, quiet intake of breath she pushed herself back into the chair.

'It's huge,' she whispered, eyes travelling from the long, smiling snout with its protruding teeth back a full ten feet to the tip of its powerful tail. With its bulging eyes and thick, bumpy hide, it looked remarkably like one of the fairy-tale dragons in a book she'd had as a child.

'It's a good size,' Cage agreed, apparently unconcerned that the boat was drifting ever closer to the bank.

Another lump opened another long set of jaws and emitted a thunderous bellow that made Melanie grip the arms of her chair even tighter. 'I think we should leave,' she hissed urgently, never taking her eyes from the group on the bank. She counted seven alligators, each one more ferocious-looking than the last.

In an abrupt scramble of motion so fast that all Melanie really saw was flying dirt and the splash of water, one of the beasts plunged into the slough and headed towards the boat.

'I think you may want to come up here with me,' Cage said calmly.

He didn't have to tell her twice. With speed born of panic, Melanie released her lap strap and scrambled up to where Cage sat at the controls. His startled look barely registered as she scurried to the other side of his chair and grasped his shoulder. His bare skin was hot under her fingers. 'Are we safe up here?' she asked breathlessly, her eyes fixed in terror on the alligator moving steadily towards the boat, only its eyes and nostrils visible above the water, its powerful tail whipping back and forth just beneath the surface.

'Safe?' Cage looked up at her, puzzled. 'Of course we're safe. I just thought you'd get a better view of him in the water from up here, that's all.'

Melanie held her breath for a moment, then released it, shoulders sagging. 'Oh,' she said in a small voice. 'I thought ... I thought ...'

'You thought it was going to climb up on the boat and eat you whole, right?' He was almost smiling.

'Something like that.'

'Well, at least you didn't faint.'

She tightened her lips, but made no reply. She was too busy watching the huge reptile circling the boat, like a buzzard waiting for the inevitable feast.

'I won't tell you that Everglades 'gators are harmless. We've had a few attacks over the years, but they don't climb up on boats. Just stay out of the water, and you'll be fine.'

'Right,' Melanie murmured, unconsciously tightening her grip on his shoulder when the alligator came so close to the boat that she couldn't see it any more.

'You don't have to be afraid,' he said quietly. 'I won't let anything hurt you.'

She looked down at her hand, at the fragile white fingers pressed deep into the sun-burnished musculature of his shoulder. She relaxed her grip a little, but couldn't bring herself to let go entirely.

'You'll feel safer sitting up here with me.' He moved sideways in the broad seat of his chair, making room.

Her head moved in a jerky nod, relieved to be as far from the water as possible. 'I'll stay up here, but I can stand.'

He left hand tapped the vinyl space next to him. 'Sit. I'm going to start the engine again, and you'll lose your balance and fall into the water...'

Melanie sat instantly, eyes wide and fixed straight ahead. She perched uncomfortably on the side of the chair, one hip on, one hip off, careful to keep a space between their bodies. She caught her breath when Cage grabbed her around the waist and pulled her against him.

'Relax,' he told her as he started the engine. 'I'm one of the creatures in this swamp that doesn't bite.'

She smiled a little, then gasped and caught his arm as the boat jerked forward.

'Sorry,' he mumbled, steadying the boat to a slow crawl. After a moment Melanie remembered to release his arm.

They rode in silence for a while, the big fan behind them whirring softly at slow speed, pushing the boat down the twisted, watery corridor. Melanie was sharply aware of the body pressed against hers. Aside from Beau, she'd never been in such close contact with a man before. It embarrassed her to feel it so keenly when his thigh muscle contracted beneath the heavy canvas trousers; to feel every degree of heat emanating from the bare skin of his arm where it pressed against the sleeve of her shirt.

Peripherally, she could see his chest rise and fall with each breath, and for a time she almost imagined she could hear the beat of his heart over the hum of the fan blade. She stole a surreptitious glance at his face once, and found it strangely insulting that his expression was totally indifferent. He doesn't even know I'm here, she thought irritably. We're pressed together like sardines in a can, and he doesn't feel a thing.

She shifted her weight on the seat intentionally and pretended to look around with nonchalance. 'Where's the alligator?'

'We left him behind long ago, but there's a water moccasin, sunning on that rock over there. Remember what he looks like. You'll want to give those snakes a wide berth.'

Instantly distracted from the press of his body, Melanie leaned forward to look past him at the brown coil on the jutting rock to their right. Her concentration totally fixed on the snake, she was oblivious to her breast brushing his bicep; to the sudden, reflexive narrowing of his eyes. 'It looks just like the one on the chair,' she said worriedly. 'I'll never be able to tell the difference.'

'You can identify a water moccasin by the inside of its mouth. It's all white. Some people call it a cottonmouth.'

They'd passed the rock by this time, and Melanie sagged back in the seat, folding her arms in disgust. 'Wonderful. I'll just get every snake I meet to open its mouth before I ask it to dance.'

He turned his head to look at her, and Melanie's scowl dissolved into an expression of unabashed wonder. He was smiling—all the way up to his eyes— and the transformation in his face took her breath away. The strength was still there, and the power; but the stern, forbidding aspect had softened into something dark and warm and incredibly seductive.

With the innocence of a child who had never felt the full, strident surge of her own sexuality, Melanie parted her lips and they curved upwards.

As focused on her countenance as she was on his, Cage relaxed his hand on the rudder and the airboat headed for the bank. His face was so close, Melanie thought in a daze; his mouth was so close; with just the smallest motion she could reach up and touch that sharp, chiselled line of his lower lip with her finger... she caught her breath at that perfectly astounding thought, and then felt herself flung forward sharply as the blunt prow jammed into the weeds on the bank. In the next instant she was flung sideways, and then his arms shot out and jerked her against his chest.

'Dammit,' he growled, leaning back far enough to look down at her face. 'Are you all right?'

She swallowed hard and nodded, gazing up into his eyes, more shaken by his closeness than she had been by the boat's thudding into the bank. His arms felt like searing bands around her; his chest felt rigid and hot beneath the soft press of her breasts. 'What happened?'

As if checking for injury, he touched her cheek with the fingertips of one hand, but at that touch took a sharp, shallow breath that flared his nostrils. His gaze dropped to her mouth and his eyes narrowed. It was only his eyes touching her lips, and yet to Melanie the glance was as searing as the press of his mouth would have been.

In a gesture as seductive as if she had consciously engineered it, she touched the centre of her lower lip with her tongue to moisten it. At that the burnished skin across his high, proud cheekbones seemed to tighten, and she felt the soft breath of an inaudible sigh brush her face. His chest swelled even as the rest of his body seemed to go rigid, and his hand tightened slightly on her back, flattening her breasts between them. She felt her nipples pucker in response to the pressure.

Had she been capable of rational thought at that moment, Melanie would have realised that the strange, hot sensations she was feeling were dangerous; that her engagement to Beau should have precluded her body's reaction to the touch of this strange, exotic-looking man; but rational thought was as far from her mind as she was from the staid, air-conditioned life she led back in civilisation.

All she knew was that right now she was feeling what those gangly, spindly-legged water birds must feel at the soaring lift of air beneath their wings. This was the exhilaration of flight; the almost unbearable ecstasy of pure physical pleasure; and anything that felt like this had to be right.

His head dipped down towards hers, blocking the sun. Their mouths were so close that, if she had spoken but a single word, their lips would have touched. And then suddenly she felt herself thrust backwards, and held rigidly at arm's length. Cage's face was dark, angry, and the quivering of tensed muscles passed through his hands into the flesh of her upper arms.

'This is crazy,' he muttered, jerking away from her and glaring straight ahead. His hands gripped the control sticks so tightly that the muscles of his fore-arms bulged with tension. 'On second thoughts, maybe you'd be safer down in the other chair.'

She felt a quiver run all the way from the base of her spine up into the back of her neck. After a hard swallow she said, 'I'll stand behind you, and hold on to your chair.' She didn't want to go back down to the lower deck, and she told herself it was because she was afraid of alligators. 'I won't get in your way,' she added in a whisper.

After what seemed like a long time he nodded once without looking at her, then gave his full attention to the controls.

They covered countless miles of inland waterways that first afternoon, and for the entire time Melanie stood directly behind Cage, her hands clutching the back of his chair, her fingers a breath away from the broad, tanned shoulders. Again and again she found herself looking down with fascination at the black sheen of his hair. It looked so smooth, almost unreal in colour and gloss. She had to fight back the impulse to touch it.

When Cage called her attention to the world around her she saw turtles and snakes and alligators and a hundred thousand birds. She heard the sound of his voice more than his words as he described their passage across broad, shallow lakes, vast sawgrass plains, and down countless narrow, twisting ribbons of water. At some point during the afternoon she forgot Beau, forgot her Tallahassee hotel-room and the family plantation in Georgia; forgot the world of automobiles and air-conditioning and computers and politics. For this tiny, single moment of her life she immersed herself totally in the present, and all the present contained was a man called Benjamin Cage and the vastness of a savage wilderness.

CHAPTER SIX

THE LATE afternoon sunlight had just begun to soften when Cage eased back on the airboat's throttle and pointed to the isolated dock just ahead. Melanie smiled at the one landmark she could recognise in all the twisted waterways of the Everglades, anticipating a shower, a reasonably comfortable chair, and, above all, food. During the course of the afternoon they'd drunk enormous quantities of metallic-tasting water from the canteens Cage carried on his belt, and they'd snacked almost continually on some kind of trail mix he kept in a metal chest on the airboat, but Melanie was still hungry. She couldn't explain the sharp increase in her appetite—she supposed it had something to do with sun and fresh air and excitement, and maybe the latitude, for all she knew.

Cage eased the boat into its mooring and gestured towards the coils of rope lying on the main platform. 'Grab one of those lines and make her fast,' he told her.

Melanie blinked at the back of his head as if he'd spoken in a foreign language. 'What?'

'I said grab one of those...'

'I heard what you said. I don't know what it means.'

He frowned at her over his shoulder. 'It means tie up the boat.'

Melanie stepped down from the pilot's platform, gingerly picked up a coil of rope, then stared uncertainly at the narrow expanse of black water between the deck and the dock.

'It's less than a foot,' he spoke impatiently. 'You won't fall in. Hurry up. I can't hold her here forever.'

Holding the rope like a lifeline, Melanie took a deep breath, jumped on to the dock, then froze when the wooden planks wiggled beneath her.

'Now make her fast.'

She looked back at Cage. His lips tightened with exasperation.

'Wrap the rope around that cleat...that metal thing right next to your left foot.'

She did as she was told, but left too much slack in the line. It dipped into the water and the boat drifted another few feet from the dock. Cage shook his head and cut the engine. After replacing the covers on the chairs, he leaped easily to the dock with the second line and crouched over one of the cleats. 'Now *this* is how to tie these. Come here and watch.' His fingers whipped the rope into a tight knot, then he tugged on the line and the knot disappeared. 'See? That's a slip-knot. It's easy. Now you try it.'

She crouched down next to him and proceeded to tie the rope into a messy jumble. She handed it back with a hapless shrug. 'Apparently I wasn't cut out to be a deckhand.'

He ignored the proffered rope and stared at her. 'You'll learn. Try again.'

After three more pathetic attempts Cage braced his arms on his thighs and looked at her. 'I thought all Southern ladies were horsewomen. Don't you ride?'

'Of course I do. I've been riding since I was——'

'Well, this is the same knot you use to tie a horse when you're grooming, or saddling up.' He studied her blank expression for a moment, then shook his head. 'Don't tell me. You never groomed or saddled your own horse, right? There were always other people to do it for you.'

She bristled a bit at his tone. 'What's wrong with that?'

'Nothing. Everything. Never mind.' He poked the end of the rope towards her again. 'Try it again. We're not leaving until you get it right.'

Melanie sighed, then attacked the rope again. Finally she managed to duplicate his knot...after a fashion. He made her do it several times before he was satisfied.

She cocked her head and examined her last effort, foolishly pleased with the way the line hugged the cleat, tightening when the boat pulled against it. 'That's good, isn't it?' She looked up to find him watching her with an odd expression.

'Yes, Melanie,' he said quietly. 'It's very good.'

Her smile blossomed under his approval, and he turned away from it, frowning. 'Come on,' he said gruffly, shading his eyes as he looked towards the sun. 'We've only got a few hours before dark.' Without another word he marched off the dock into the brush.

Melanie stared after him a moment in dumb surprise before scampering behind to keep him in sight. He led her around the waterline back into the forest while she trotted to match his long strides. He never spoke, he never glanced over his shoulder to make sure she was still behind him, and the pace he set was so fast that she was exhausted after just a few moments.

What does he think I am, she thought irritably—a marathon runner? She followed doggedly, too breathless to complain, scowling at his back as she dodged the enormous trunks of the ancient trees. It was cooler under their shade than it had been in the open, but the air was still heavy with humidity and before long her T-shirt clung damply to her skin. Without breaking stride she slipped off the heavy overshirt and tied the sleeves around her waist, leaving her arms bare.

Almost immediately a swarm of tiny, biting flies appeared from nowhere to light on her arms, and the forest silence was broken by the sound of her hands slapping at them.

'Put that back on.' He'd stopped and turned to face her, and Melanie was so intent on brushing the bugs from her arms that she nearly ran right into him.

'It's hot,' she complained, scowling at his bare arms. 'Why aren't the bugs landing on you?'

He shrugged and started untying the sleeves at her waist. 'I'm a businessman, not an entomologist. Maybe they like your perfume.' Still facing her, he held the shirt open behind her shoulders while she slipped her arms into the sleeves. His eyes dropped briefly to the dip of her cleavage rising above the low-cut T-shirt. 'They say insects are attracted to the female hormone.'

Melanie blushed and pulled the front panels of the shirt closed. Her hands froze when she saw how intently he watched her working the buttons. His eyes jerked upwards, met hers, then he spun on his heel and strode away.

They reached the cabin in another five minutes, and Melanie paused at the bottom of the steps to catch her breath. Thanks to the pace Cage had set, she was hot, sweaty, and exhausted; a totally alien condition for her.

'What's the matter? What are you waiting for?' He had stepped aside to let her climb the stairs first.

'I have half a mind to make you carry me up these steps after that work-out...' she started to grumble, then gasped when he swept her effortlessly into his arms and started trotting up the steps. 'Good lord, put me down. What are you doing?'

'Stop wriggling.' He nudged the screen door open with his shoulder and walked inside, like a groom carrying his bride over the threshold.

'Very funny. You can put me down now.'

He turned his head slowly and looked directly into her eyes. He didn't say anything, and he made no move to release her.

'Uh...Mr Cage...'

'You shouldn't have taken off your hat.' His voice seemed to rumble through his body into hers. 'Your face is sunburned.' He set her down then jerked his hands away, as if he'd suddenly remembered she was too hot to touch. 'We'll want to shower before it gets dark. You first.'

She nodded wordlessly and backed away towards the bed and her suitcases. He remained motionless where he stood, watching her.

'Soap and towels are in the chest at the foot of the bed. You remember how to run the shower?'

'I remember.' She turned and started to rummage through her suitcase, but she could feel his eyes on her back. It was a relief when she heard him turn and walk towards the makeshift counter-top on the far wall.

With increasing dismay she sorted through and rejected almost every article of clothing she had brought. What did you wear for a night in a primitive cabin without running water or electricity? A beaded cocktail dress? That stupid sundress with the low bodice and full skirt that Beau said photographed so well? She finally pulled her silk summer robe out of the case and slung it over her arm. It was more of a caftan, really; a shapeless ankle-length garment with big sleeves and a loosely fitted scooped neckline. She'd never dreamed she'd wear such a thing in company—she'd brought it along for wearing around the hotel-room—but at least it was comfortable, and the peaches and blues of the big floral pattern were a bright, welcome change from the drab colours she'd worn all day.

Once downstairs she stood in the shelter of the porch and looked around for a long time. The daytime sounds of the Everglades were muted by late afternoon, and the quality of light filtering through the giant trees had changed, become almost golden.

Dragonflies as large as her hand dipped transparent wings into the fading sunlight as they soared past, and even the ugly bluebottle flies took on an iridescent beauty in the softer light.

Melanie blew out a long, quiet sigh. She'd never undressed outside before, and it wasn't mere modesty that made her reluctant now. There was an awful vulnerability about being naked without the security of walls around you. She shifted her shoulders nervously, felt the sweat-dampened shirt chafe her skin, and stripped quickly out of her clothes, tossing them into a pile.

She stood there for a moment before opening the
nozzle of the hose, shivering in spite of the heat,
goosebumps rising all over her body. And then she
giggled. She *had* been naked outside once before—
she remembered now. All of three or four years old,
just out of the family pool, she'd run from her nanny's
arms, peeled off her tiny swimsuit, and raced buck-
naked across the expansive lawns, shrieking with delight at the sense of freedom; at the glorious feeling
of absolutely nothing between her skin and the world
outside. Unconsciously she rubbed her right buttock,
remembering the gentle slap from her nanny's hand
and the verbal rebuke that had shamed her for such
unladylike behaviour. She'd never done such a thing
again. Until now.

She smiled a little as she opened the hose nozzle
and let the tepid water soak her hair and sluice over
her body. She could hear Cage's footsteps in the cabin
above when she turned off the hose to lather her hair
and skin.

Attracted by the prism of sunlight through the
bubbles, a dragonfly lighted on her forearm, and she
touched the edge of one of its four wings delicately,
marvelling when it didn't fly away. Entranced that
such a fragile creature could be so fearless, she waited
until it took flight again before opening the hose
nozzle to rinse herself.

Cage looked up from something he was doing at
the counter when she came back inside. His black eyes
swept from the hem of the brightly coloured robe up
to her dripping hair, then fixed on her face. 'You took
a long time.'

'Sorry,' Melanie smiled sheepishly. 'A dragonfly
landed on my arm—it actually landed on my arm...'

The childish excitement in her voice trailed away at his perplexed expression. 'Anyway, I didn't want to frighten it,' she finished in a mumble.

It nearly bowled her over when he smiled, and, as she gazed at that proud, rigid countenance suddenly softening with the gentle grin an adult reserved for a very young child, she thought that she had never really seen a genuine smile until she'd seen his.

'I won't be long.' He gathered a stack of clothing from a chair and passed close to her as he went outside. The air stirred at his passage, brushing Melanie's face like a whisper that smelled like sunlight. 'There's water in the jug and some snacks on the counter. Help yourself.'

He wasn't halfway down the outside steps when her stomach growled noisily. While he showered downstairs she stood at the counter and ate peanuts out of the bowl, then attacked a plate of cheese and some sort of crisp corn cracker. Everything was unbelievably delicious, and after a few moments she stopped and looked at the rapidly emptying dishes with dismay. If she didn't slow down there wouldn't be anything left for Cage.

She sighed, touched a finger to the bridge of her nose, then shrugged and drained the icy fruit drink in the tall glass next to the food. This time she heard the soft steps of his feet on the stairs, and wondered if she was becoming attuned to the sound.

'Good lord,' he said from the doorway, eyes on the empty glass in her hand. 'You drink like a longshoreman.'

'Salty food,' she said, staring at him openly. His hair was wet and shiny black, dripping water on to a thin white cotton shirt open at the neck. He was wearing snug, faded blue jeans, and his brown feet were bare.

He walked over and took her glass, staring at it as if he couldn't believe it was empty. 'I thought we covered this once today. You eat salty food here to replace what you lose in perspiration, but drink *water* to quench your thirst. Not this stuff.'

She blinked at him, confused. 'You said to help myself...'

'To the water in the jug.' He pointed at a large Thermos container next to some empty glasses. 'Not to my drink.'

'Oh. Sorry I drank yours. It was good.' She smiled up at him broadly. 'Water, fruit juice...what difference does it make? It's all liquid...' She frowned hard, wondering why she suddenly felt so warm.

'That "fruit juice" was almost half vodka, and you just drank it without taking a breath,' he informed her. 'How do you feel?'

Her eyes widened slightly. 'Oh, dear. Vodka? Well. I must have more of a tolerance for alcohol than I thought, because I feel fine. Just fine.' She had the sinking feeling she was grinning again. 'Why? Do I look funny?' She couldn't imagine why she'd asked him that, but for some reason her mind couldn't fix on the question long enough to find an answer.

He pressed his lips together hard. 'You look...' His black brows twitched towards one another in a pained expression.

'Nevermind.' Melanie made a face when the words ran together. 'Never *mind*,' she amended. 'I know how I look. Bedraggled. No make-up, wet hair, good heavens, it's hot, isn't it?' She plucked the bodice of her robe away from her chest. 'I don't drink alcohol, as a rule,' she said importantly.

'Really?'

'No, really. I don't. Maybe a little wine with dinner, but never more than that, because . . .' She cocked her head, frowning hard, trying to remember why ladies never drank more than a little wine with dinner.

'Melanie.'

She looked up at him seriously. 'Benjamin.'

He rolled his eyes and tried to scowl at her. 'Go sit down,' he said firmly. 'Way over there. I'll bring you something to eat.'

With exaggerated care, Melanie walked obediently to the chair next to the sofa and sat down. 'Is this far enough?'

'Probably not,' he said without turning around from whatever he was doing at the counter. She smiled, thinking again how melodic his voice was; deep and rich and lulling, in spite of the hard northern accent.

'Where are you from?' she asked idly, lifting one foot to admire her red cloth slipper, wondering why she'd never noticed how pretty the colour was before.

'Right here. Florida.'

'You don't talk like a Southerner.'

He shrugged carelessly, still working at the counter. 'My mom left us when I was a kid, and I guess Dad went a little crazy. He said he couldn't stand living in the place they'd lived in together, so we moved north to Chicago.'

'Your mother just . . . left you?' Even through the pleasant fuzz cushioning her thoughts, Melanie was appalled. Her own experience had taught her the pain of being a motherless child; but to be motherless because the mother had simply walked away...? She couldn't imagine the kinds of scars that would leave on a young psyche. 'Did you ever see her again?'

Cage shrugged again, as if that were the only gesture he could remember how to perform. 'No. Never saw her, never heard from her, never wanted to.'

Melanie cringed at the bitterness in his voice. 'What about your father? Didn't he try to contact her...?'

'My father was a fool,' he snapped, and Melanie cringed at the contempt in his voice. 'He died years later, when I was fourteen, but the truth is he'd stopped living the day she walked out of his life.'

'When did you finally come back to Florida?' she asked carefully.

'I started hitch-hiking back down here the day I buried my father...'

'When you were *fourteen*?'

He sighed impatiently. 'I was old enough. I lied about my age, worked the groves during the day, and finished school at night. By the time I was eighteen I had my first orchard.'

Melanie blinked, finding such independence frightening, almost incomprehensible. She was twenty-four, and had trouble deciding what to wear in the morning. She remembered Beau's words about Cage clawing his way to the top on his own. No wonder he seemed so self-contained; so distant. 'You barely had a childhood,' she murmured.

He walked over and set a plate of food in her lap. 'That's enough ancient history. Here. Eat every bite. I'll start some coffee.'

She stared after him, struggling to keep her thoughts focused on the image of Cage as a young boy, living alone, forced to leap suddenly into adulthood...

He turned back and scowled at her. 'Eat!' he commanded, shattering her already weakened concentration.

She sighed and looked down at her plate, speared a piece of cold meat, eyed it sceptically, then placed it in her mouth. 'Good,' she said perfunctorily, happy for an excuse to change the subject. 'I hope it's not something you caught outside.'

He chuckled softly. 'It's chicken, marinated in a herb dressing, then roasted and chilled. I brought it from home for my first meal with the congressman.'

'Oh.' Melanie stared glumly at the colourful pile of baby carrots and bright green snap beans, unhappy at the reminder that she was not the guest of choice.

Cage brought his plate to the couch opposite her, and they finished the meal in silence while the aroma of coffee perking on the camp stove filled the cabin. After her second full cup, Melanie's mind was perfectly, painfully clear again. She hadn't realised how dark the room had become until Cage got up to light the oil lamps. They smoked for a moment, then cast a beautiful golden glow within their small circles of light. There was one on the counter next to the stack of dirty dishes, one on a small table between the couch and the chair, and another near the bed.

'How do you feel now?' he asked her, leaning over from the couch to fill her cup for the third time.

She looked across the small space between them. The lamp flickered in an unseen breath of wind, making shadows dance on his dark face. He sat with one knee cocked, foot on the couch cushion, his arm stretched over the back. 'Sober,' she replied, and then added in a small voice, 'unfortunately.'

He smiled a little at that. 'Why "unfortunately"?'

She looked down into her cup and sighed. 'I don't know. Maybe because, for a time, I forgot who I was and what I was doing here, and it all just seemed like some wonderful child's adventure.'

'The Everglades *is* an adventure.'

She smiled sadly. 'After a drink or two it's an adventure. Stone-cold sober, it's a terrifying, alien place to someone like me. The women in my family weren't bred to be very daring, I'm afraid.'

'That's the second time today you've said something like that. You're kidding, of course.'

Melanie's look was a question.

'What about the woman you were named for? They don't come much more daring than that.'

Melanie felt her whole body go still. 'I was named for my great-great-great-grandmother,' she said carefully.

'When you told me your full name I assumed you were one of her descendants. Still, it was a shock...' He shook his head with a funny little smile. 'Melanie Annabelle Brooks, wife of Henry Albert Brooks of Creek County, Georgia...do you have any idea what the odds must be against her namesake showing up down here?'

Melanie stared at him, blue eyes wide and mystified, wondering how he could possibly know the names of her ancestors.

'They still talk about her, naturally. It's part of——'

'They?' she interrupted sharply.

'The Seminole Indians, of course. Who did you think?'

Melanie couldn't stop staring at him, as if she could pull the knowledge she craved from the black depths of his eyes. She felt the strident pounding of her heart, the wild surge of anticipation coursing through her veins like a shot of adrenalin. All her life she'd been searching for a single scrap of information about the woman in the old oil portrait, and now, impossible as it seemed, a stranger was going to fill in the blanks in her own family history. She licked her lips and spoke carefully. 'You know about my great-great-great-grandmother?'

'Well, of course. She's a legend down here.'

The chirping of insects filled the silence that followed, and to Melanie the darkness outside seemed to be creeping into the cabin, trying to obliterate the tiny circles of light.

Slowly, balancing her cup on her lap, her eyes fixed on his face, she leaned forward in her chair. 'Tell me,' she whispered. 'Tell me what you know about her.'

'You want me to tell you about your own ancestor?' he asked, confused. 'I'm sure you know more...'

'No. I don't know anything about her, except what she looked like, and that her own husband crossed her name out of the family Bible.' She shuddered. 'I still hate to think about that. It's almost as if he tried to...erase her.'

Cage's expression hardened. 'He actually did that? Crossed out her name?'

Melanie nodded.

He sighed heavily and looked off to one side. 'I suppose that was to be expected back then...' he murmured, then looked at her, his gaze sharp. 'And you really don't know anything about her? No family stories? No journals?'

'Nothing. I found her portrait in the attic when I was a kid, but if it weren't for that, it would be as if she never existed at all.'

His eyes softened a little, reflecting the lamplight. 'What did she look like?'

Melanie glanced down at her lap. 'Like...me.' When she looked up again he was smiling.

'The legend says she gave shelter to one of Osceola's warriors when the government troops were hunting them down during the uprising of 1835...'

She frowned hard, scouring her memory for old school lessons in history. Osceola...who was Osceola? She shook her head, passing over the question for the time being. It would come to her eventually. 'Go on,' she encouraged him.

He studied her face silently for a moment. 'She was here, you know,' he said quietly.

'Here?'

'In the Everglades.'

'But that's crazy. It's hundreds of miles from Creek County. It would have taken days, maybe weeks to make that trip in a carriage, and why would she have come in the first place...?'

'That's the legend. Part of Seminole history, handed down by word of mouth from generation to generation.'

Melanie sagged against the back of her chair, her thoughts numb. Her eyes drifted to the blackness outside the screen, as if she could see the savage land encroaching on the cabin. 'It would have been even more wild then,' she murmured, more to herself than to Cage, entranced by the notion that she might not be the first Brooks woman to see this place; that the first would have worn full, floor-length dresses in this

impossible heat; that her shoes would have been soled
with thin leather that let the water seep in; that she
would have slept on the ground with the snakes and
chased insects with a silk fan. Suddenly she felt foolish
and spoiled and unconscionably helpless.

'Why?' she whispered. 'Why would she come to
the Everglades?'

Cage stared at her. 'If you're really interested,
tomorrow I'll take you to someone who can answer
that. Someone who knows all the old legends.'

She almost wrung her hands in frustration.
Tomorrow was a million years away.

'It's dark, Melanie,' he said gently. 'You're going
to have enough trouble finding your way to the outhouse and back, let alone going deeper into the
'Glades.'

'Oh, dear.' She made a woeful face at the reminder
of things a little more immediate than learning about
her ancestor. Sun and sweat had taken care of the
water they'd had during the afternoon, but all the
liquid she'd drunk this evening was another matter.
'I forgot about the outhouse.'

He smiled at her. 'It's a long way in the dark your
first time. You want an escort?'

It must be just a little bit wicked, Melanie thought
later, spending the night with a man you'd just met.
But it didn't feel wicked. As she lay in the only bed,
arms crossed under her head, eyes staring up into the
darkness, she felt as deliciously giddy as a young girl
on her first trip to summer camp.

Within the short space of a single day the world
had opened like a Christmas package filled with pos-
sibilities. She'd done things she'd never dreamed of

doing; seen things she'd never expected to see; felt things she hadn't known she was capable of feeling ... her mind slammed shut abruptly on those particular thoughts and she blushed in the dark.

And tomorrow—she tried to shift her mind's direction—tomorrow you'll have answers to questions you've been asking for years. Who was the first Melanie Annabelle Brooks? What had she been like? What terrible thing had she done to cause her memory to be nearly obliterated? And why had she come here?

She shivered with anticipation, listening to the sounds of an insect symphony outside the screens, syncopated by the throaty croaking of frogs. Occasionally there was a distant, muted bellow—alligators talking, Cage had told her. He'd called it the night music of the Everglades, making her smile at his poetic phrasing.

He'd been a perfect gentleman on that first embarrassing trip to the outhouse, lighting the path with his flashlight, then leaving it with her while he went back to the cabin to give her privacy. She'd imagined giant snakes and ravenous alligators lying in wait on the path, and had scurried back to the cabin steps with her heart thumping. The truth was she would gladly have sacrificed privacy for the security of his presence on the return trip, and she imagined that the early pioneer women must have felt the same way about their men.

He was asleep now in his sleeping-bag, over by the sofa. She'd heard the sounds of clothing hitting the floor in the dark, and couldn't help but wonder how much he'd taken off, and how much he'd left on. For herself, she'd been perfectly comfortable stripping out of her robe and crawling into bed in only a short

cotton nightie. The utter blackness of a world away
from city lights made her feel invisible, satisfying
whatever sense of modesty that had survived the walk
to the outhouse. Besides, it was still too hot and humid
to wear anything but the barest necessity. Even the
weight of the sheet on her bare limbs seemed stifling,
but she didn't dare kick it off in case Cage woke first
in the morning, before she had a chance to cover
herself decently.

'Having trouble falling asleep?'

She started at the unexpected sound of his voice,
like a kid caught up past her bedtime. 'A little,' she
said after a beat. 'How did you know I was still
awake?'

'Your breathing.'

She thought about that for a moment, her pulse
quickening to know he'd been lying there all this time,
listening to her breathe.

'Is the bed uncomfortable?'

'No, it's fine. I don't know what it is. Over-
excitement, I suppose. It's been quite a day.'

They were both whispering, as if the camp coun-
sellor would barge in any minute and scold them for
talking past lights out.

'Cage?' she whispered, wondering why she'd auto-
matically chosen his last name rather than his first.
She decided it was because Benjamin didn't suit him.
It was too...ordinary.

'What, Melanie?'

There was something magic about hearing her name
spoken in the dark. It made her smile. 'This is...fun.'

Silence for a beat, and then softly, 'Fun?'

She sighed noisily. 'I know. It's a child's word, and
it doesn't sound very professional...but I just can't

think of another. I've never done anything like this, you know. I never rode in one of those boats; I never saw an alligator or used an outhouse or—good heavens—I never even had too much to drink before.' She paused and frowned up at the ceiling she couldn't see. 'It's just been the most extraordinary day,' she finished softly.

When he didn't say anything in response, she thought he'd probably fallen asleep after all. She turned her head and squinted through the blackness at where he lay on the floor, but it was too dark and too far away to see anything clearly. Surely it was only her imagination that made her think she saw two spots of light where his face might have been; the kind of light that might come from the moist surfaces of eyes held open, staring up at the ceiling.

She flopped on to her back with a sigh, and then realised that at this moment, lying here in a pitch-black primitive cabin in the middle of the wilderness, she was happier than she'd ever been. The realisation troubled her, and she rolled on to her side, resigned to spending the entire night awake worrying about it. Within moments she was sound asleep, and a short time later her subconscious mind directed her foot to kick the offending sheet off her body.

Cage turned his head silently at the sound and narrowed his eyes in the dark.

CHAPTER SEVEN

MELANIE was teased awake by the aroma of fresh
coffee and the homy sound of sausages sizzling in a
hot skillet. The smells and sounds conjured up the
lazy weekend mornings of her childhood in Georgia,
and she stretched and yawned with a child's sense of
well-being.

'Good morning.'

Her eyes jerked and focused past her bare toes to
where Benjamin Cage stood over the camp stove on
the counter, creating the heavenly aromas that filled
the cabin. He wore cut-off jeans and nothing else,
and she looked away quickly from his broad, tanned
back. Even after such a brief glance, the image of
him remained etched in her mind. She still saw the
shiny black hair swept back; the interlacing of muscle
across the shoulders, sloping down to meet the indentation of his spine.

'Good morning,' she mumbled, thinking that the
least he could have done was dress decently. It was
unthinkable that a man who barely knew her should
parade in her presence half-naked ...

The thought had barely formed when she glanced
down at her own body, and swallowed a horrified
gasp. The sheet was in a tangle at the foot of the bed,
and her cotton nightie was bunched up over her ribs,
exposing a good deal of flesh above the matching scrap
of panty.

She sat up quickly, jerked her nightie down, and grabbed for her robe.

'Too late,' Cage chuckled without turning around. 'I've already seen you in your nightgown. I suppose that means we'll have to get married.'

Melanie jammed her arms into the sleeves of her robe, blushing furiously.

He turned and smiled lazily over his shoulder at the clatter she made scrambling for her tennis shoes. 'You've got five minutes before breakfast if you want to wash first.'

She nodded brusquely, grabbed her cosmetic case and a flannel and headed for the outside steps. She froze on the top one and stared, caught off guard by the wild sensation of being so high in the middle of a forest. She'd forgotten as she'd slept, or perhaps she'd been too preoccupied yesterday to fully appreciate the view from this height.

It wasn't the kind of scenery that sold property— no mountain vistas, no golden plains stretching for the horizon—but there was something magical about looking straight into the leafy canopy that sheltered the forest floor. It *was* a tree-house, she mused, her eyes searching for the source of a raucous cawing, finally focusing on a nearby branch. A bright green bird perched there on the edge of her nest, ministering to scrawny, open-mouthed fledgelings. Melanie couldn't help but smile.

'That's a green jay,' Cage said from behind her as he walked out to join her on the porch. 'They make a terrible racket in the morning. I was surprised you slept through it.'

'They're beautiful,' Melanie murmured, pulling in a deep breath of the clean, golden morning air. 'Everything's beautiful from up here.'

She felt his eyes on her as he moved to her side, and wondered how she could be aware of that when she wasn't looking. She let her eyes fall closed, as if testing the limits of all her senses except sight. Curiously, she felt Cage's presence much as she would feel the weightless warmth of sunlight on her skin. She remembered feeling stifled sometimes when Beau came too close, and then frowned at the way she'd phrased her thoughts. Beau was her fiancé. She shouldn't ever think of him as 'too' close—and yet when he approached he seemed to push the air against her, like a strong wind battering a wall. It was so unlike Cage standing here, his bare arm a hair's breadth away, his nearness moving the air in a soft breath that seemed to circle her like the lovely tendrils of a warm mist.

She knew when his eyes left her to look out over the canopy; she felt the absence of his gaze as keenly as she had felt its touch. 'I think I love it here,' she murmured, before she even knew she was going to say it.

'Do you?' he asked quietly, but it was more confirmation than question, almost as if he had expected she would see the beauty here, if she only looked closely enough.

Like the carefully choreographed movement of two dancers, their heads turned and their eyes met. 'But only up here,' she added with a chagrined smile. 'I'm still afraid of almost everything on the ground in this place.'

She felt the protectiveness of his smile more than she saw it; felt it lifting her up until she wondered if her feet still touched the wooden floor. 'You're safer in the Everglades than you are on the streets of any major city in the world. The only really frightening thing here—or anywhere, for that matter—is man.' He turned his head to look out over the canopy again. 'Everything else here has been the same for centuries. Like this particular stand of trees. It's one of the old-growth forests that man hasn't touched yet, and it looks pretty much the same way it did hundreds of years ago. If your ancestral grandmother travelled this way, you're seeing what she saw.'

Melanie felt a flutter of excitement at the reminder that today she would learn something of her own history, and that, ironically, it was all part of this strange place she had always thought of as alien and frightening.

'Breakfast is almost ready,' Cage reminded her gently, and she heard in his voice a reluctance to have the moment end.

'I'll hurry,' she said quietly, but she moved slowly towards the door and the stairs, totally comfortable with his eyes on her back as she walked away. It oc-curred to her briefly that comfort was the last thing she should be feeling with Benjamin Cage. He wasn't supposed to be the kind of man that inspired comfort—he was supposed to be an unreasonable zealot; a radical; a man you simply couldn't talk to, Beau had said.

But Beau had lied. She stopped halfway down the steps as the words popped into her mind with the sud-denness of a gunshot, threatening to shred the very fabric of the life that had been so carefully planned for her. She stood immobile for a moment, struggling with a dizzy sensation that had come out of nowhere. Suddenly the green jay squawked over her head, and thoughts of Beau and her dizziness vanished at the same instant. Neither belonged here.

She caught herself smiling as she walked back from the outhouse towards the hose that snaked down from the rain barrel—maybe because she hadn't been eaten by any ferocious reptilian monsters—or maybe because there was something energising about running around outside in your housecoat and washing your face in a hollowed-out log. Her face stung a bit as she splashed the soap away, and she remembered Cage telling her she was sunburned.

A circle of reflective tin was nailed to one of the cabin's support posts close to the hose, and she moved towards it, realising that she hadn't looked into a mirror since yesterday. Her appearance had always seemed such a crucial part of her life; how strange that within the space of a single day all that had changed. She thought about that as she peered into the shiny circle of tin while she brushed her long blonde hair back from her face. No make-up, no hairspray, no perfectly co-ordinated outfit, and yet somehow she didn't think she looked that bad. The sunburn was mild, making her appear flushed more than burned, and the added colour made her eyes rival the blue of the sky peeping through the treetops.

'Come on!' Cage called from overhead, and she gathered her things and hurried up the steps.

He'd brought folding chairs out to the porch and they ate there, plates balanced on their laps, coffee-mugs held in their free hands, eyes wandering the world around them. It was the first time Melanie could ever remember eating in her housecoat, and there was something wonderfully decadent about that.

'I could get used to your cooking,' she told him, spearing the last piece of fluffy scrambled egg with her fork and popping it into her mouth.

'You probably won't feel that way after supper tonight. The cooler is only good for a day or two of reliable refrigeration in this heat. I'm afraid we're down to canned goods now.'

She shrugged, unconcerned. 'It doesn't matter. Everything seems to taste wonderful here.' She felt his eyes on her in the silence that followed, and finally looked up to find him staring at her with the most peculiar, speculative expression.

'You don't look much like the woman who got off that plane yesterday,' he said quietly.

Melanie laughed. 'I'm quite sure of that...' She sobered suddenly. 'Was that an insult?'

'Definitely not.'

'Good.' She balanced her empty plate on her lap and cradled her mug in both hands, staring off into the forest canopy. 'I don't feel much like the woman who arrived here yesterday.'

'What's different?'

She glanced at him to see if the question was serious before answering with a chuckle, 'Everything. I feel like an impostor, pretending to be myself.'

He laughed at that.

'It's true. Yesterday I was prim and proper Melanie Brooks of the Creek County social register; today...' she shrugged eloquently '...today I'm some wild woman who showers with dragonflies and eats breakfast in her housecoat...stop laughing. You can't imagine how out of character I am.'

'Are you?' he asked quietly, and she turned to look at him, her face as serious as his tone had been. 'Maybe that woman in the social register was the one who was out of character.'

She was just starting to think about that when he smiled suddenly and leaned back in his chair, crossing his legs at the ankles. 'This is nice,' he said.

'What is?'

'This. Sharing breakfast. Sharing the morning here. I've never done that before. I didn't expect to enjoy it so much.'

'Neither did I,' she murmured, then caught her lower lip between her teeth. She shouldn't have said that; she probably shouldn't even have thought it. 'I mean I didn't expect to enjoy a fact-finding trip,' she tried to disguise the intimacy of what she had really meant. 'This isn't what I thought it would be like . . .' She frowned hard and let the sentence fade away.

'You expected cocktail parties and slide shows.'

'Yes,' she said with quick relief.

'And you didn't expect to like me.'

She hesitated. 'No. I didn't.' He smiled easily, lazily, somehow relieving the tension so that Melanie could smile, too. 'And I expected to be lectured,' she added. 'Shouldn't you be doing that? Itemising all the reasons the budget for Everglades protection shouldn't be cut?'

He shrugged. 'The idea is that, after you spend some time here, the reasons will become apparent. I'll answer your questions; I'll even volunteer some information; but, if I start to lecture, stop me. Seeing for yourself, doing for yourself—lectures can't compete with that kind of hands-on learning.'

'You should be a teacher.'

'That's the role I'm playing this weekend. I'm your teacher, and the Everglades is the lesson and the classroom, all rolled into one. You've already learned a lot. You just don't realise it yet.'

There was silence between them for a time; a comfortable, restful silence as they both absorbed the peace of their surroundings, and Melanie wondered what he thought she had learned. He might be surprised, she mused, because the lessons so far had taught her more about herself than about the Everglades.

'I've been trying to remember my old school lessons,' Melanie said at last. 'I don't think Osceola was much more than a paragraph in an American history text. He was a rogue warrior of the Seminole Indian tribe back in the 1800s, right?'

He turned his head to look at her, one brow arched. 'Some called him a rogue. Do you remember why?'

Her brow furrowed in concentration. 'I remember something about the government trying to move all the Seminoles out of Florida to a reservation somewhere, but Osceola refused to leave his home. He started a rebellion, didn't he?'

Cage looked at her steadily. 'A war, actually. Osceola and a small number of renegade warriors against the entire US Army.'

Melanie smiled sadly. 'Sounds as if the odds were a little uneven.'

'A little.'

She eyed him intently. 'Are you trying to tell me that my ancestral grandmother actually knew Osceola?'

'Maybe,' he shrugged. 'That's not clear in the legend. Only that she hid one of his wounded warriors from government troops.'

Melanie sighed hard and looked off into the distance, frowning. 'I find that very hard to believe. The Indians were killing settlers back then. They were savages.'

He looked at her for a long moment. 'The white men were also killing Indians. Perhaps the Indians thought *they* were savages.'

She pondered the logic of that for a moment, then conceded the possibility with a slight nod. 'With that kind of prejudice on both sides, it makes it even harder to imagine a white woman meeting a Seminole warrior, let alone hiding one from government troops...'

'Get dressed, Melanie,' he interrupted her gently. 'I think it's time I took you to meet the one person who can tell you the legend word for word, just as it was told to her.'

Melanie leaned forward in her chair. 'It's a woman?'

Cage nodded and smiled. 'A very old Seminole woman. Now go get ready. I'll clear up the dishes while you dress.'

Melanie dressed hurriedly, almost oblivious to Cage at the nearby counter, his back turned. If she'd thought about it she would have found her adjustment to the current circumstances quite amazing. Yesterday she couldn't imagine surviving without indoor plumbing and privacy; today she'd used an outhouse without a second thought, and was now dressing within a few feet of a man she'd known for less than twenty-four hours.

She pulled on a new pair of the heavy canvas trousers, then, after a token glance to ensure Cage's back was still turned, slipped her nightgown over her head and pulled on a fresh T-shirt. Back in Tallahassee, being seen in such a top would have been unthinkable; being seen in such a top without a bra beneath would have been downright indecent. It occurred to her then that Beau would be horrified to see her like this—but then Beau had never spent an afternoon trudging through a steamy rain forest with bra straps chafing his shoulders.

'Are you decent?' Cage said without turning around.

Melanie looked down with a wry expression at the clear outline of breast and nipple under the thin cotton. 'I suppose that would depend on whom you asked.'

'I'm asking you.'

She slipped her arms quickly into the long sleeves of a clean overshirt and pulled it closed over her breasts. 'Now I am.' She sat on the bed and started to put on the hot rubber boots. 'Do we really need boots today?'

'I'm afraid so.' He went to the chest at the foot of the bed and pulled clean clothing from beneath the towels. 'When we get to where we're going you can take them off and go barefoot.'

Melanie stifled a giggle at the perfectly preposterous image of Congressman Beau Parker's fiancée barefoot *and* braless.

'I don't know about that...' she started to say, glancing up at Cage. Her jaw dropped open at the same moment Cage dropped his cut-off jeans to the floor. Totally oblivious to her wide-eyed astonishment, clad only in black briefs, he stepped into a pair of canvas trousers like hers and hopped once as he pulled them up. He caught sight of her expression just as he was about to pull on a black T-shirt and froze.

'What's wrong?'

She blinked once and swallowed, gesturing mindlessly with one hand at the crumpled cut-offs on the floor.

'What?' he whispered, still immobile, moving only his eyes to examine the floor. 'What?' he spat again, jerking his eyes up in a wary question.

Melanie cleared her throat, embarrassed. 'Well...you just...took off your pants. Right in front of me.'

'Oh, for crying out loud,' he muttered, his whole body sagging with a sigh of relief, then he finished jerking on the T-shirt and snapped at her, 'Dammit, don't ever do that again! I thought I was about to step on a snake.'

'Well, pardon me,' she snapped back. 'I just don't happen to be accustomed to men undressing right in front of me.'

'Really. And what does Congressman Parker do? Go to bed fully clothed?'

'I'm sure I wouldn't know,' she fired back haughtily. The moment the words were out of her mouth, she wished she hadn't revealed so much.

'*What*?'

Melanie ignored him, pretending to concentrate on buttoning her shirt. Even in the heavy rubber boots, he barely made a sound walking around the bed to stand in front of where she sat. She stared straight ahead at the mud-green of his trouser legs.

'Are you saying that you and the congressman don't...?'

Her head jerked up and her eyes flashed angrily. 'That's really none of your business, is it?'

Cage stared down at her, his black eyes sharp and intrusive. 'A little defensive, aren't you? Is that because you are sleeping with him, or because you aren't?'

It felt as if all the heat of all the Everglades summers had settled in Melanie's face. She swallowed hard and looked away, wondering why it bothered her so much for him to know she wasn't just inexperienced at tying knots—she was inexperienced at everything. 'Are we ready to go yet?'

He was silent for what seemed like a very long time. 'I'll fill the canteens.'

She closed her eyes and released an enormous sigh of relief when he turned away.

They walked away from the cabin in the opposite direction they had taken the day before, Cage leading the way through the dark hush of the cathedral-like pine forest. Melanie followed silently, her thoughts turned inwards.

Times have certainly changed, she thought miserably. In my mother's day, having sex before the wedding-day was one of those dark, humiliating secrets you prayed would never get out. And here I am, embarrassed to admit that it *hasn't* happened. Not that I think it's essential, of course. There's absolutely nothing wrong with saving yourself for marriage; in fact, there's something very pure and admirable about the virgin bride—but isn't holding on to your virginity supposed to be at least a little bit of a challenge? Aren't men supposed to be driven by their passion? Out of control most of the time, with only the strong will of the woman keeping them at bay?

She watched the steady placement of her feet on the forest path, frowning hard. Beau had *never* been out of control; as a matter of fact, *he* had been the one to take her shoulders and push her gently away when their kisses had become too prolonged. So what did that mean? That he didn't love her? Or simply that she wasn't the kind of woman who inspired men to passion?

She sighed heavily and glanced up at Cage's back a short distance ahead. Do I inspire him? she wondered, staring at where the thin material of his T-shirt was already clinging to the indentation of his spine. She recalled the moments of physical contact they'd had yesterday—on the airboat when they'd run into the bank; in the cabin after he'd carried her up the stairs. A dark, heavy flutter rippled from breast to stomach when she recalled the heat in his eyes; but then she remembered that each time he'd put her from him, almost as an afterthought. Her mouth twitched irritably, thinking that Cage didn't have any trouble keeping his hands off her, either. Maybe no man would.

'Melanie?'

'Hmm?'

'Come up here and walk next to me.'

She hung back sullenly. 'I'm following in your footsteps, just as I was directed yesterday. Have you forgotten? I'm the one who follows orders so well.'

He ignored the crack and slowed until she came alongside. 'There are no hidden bogs on this trail. It's safe to walk next to me.'

'If you say so.'

He suppressed a smile. 'You're very quiet. What are you thinking about?'

'I'm not thinking. I'm absorbing the environment. I'm fact-finding. That's why I'm here, remember?'

'I remember.'

They both stopped and looked up as their passage disturbed a flock of small, colourful birds roosting overhead.

'We're walking inland now,' he said, moving forward again, 'towards a small stream where I keep a canoe. The airboat's too big for the waterways we'll take today.'

'I thought all of the Everglades was under water; that you could take an airboat anywhere.'

'Not any more. They've drained a lot of it. Originally it was five times larger than it is today.'

Melanie looked down at the animal trail they were following and saw the one thing she'd never expected to see in the country's biggest freshwater marsh—little dust clouds rising around her boots. 'They're draining the Everglades?'

'They don't call it draining—they call it water management.'

'Oh, *that*. I read about the water-management programme. It's very scientifically controlled; very carefully monitored to minimise damage to the Everglades ecosystem,' she quoted some of the literature Beau had given her to read.

'Right,' he said drily. 'They very scientifically decide how much land to drain for housing developments, how much water they can get away with diverting to the big agricultural fields up north...'

'None of that is hurting the Everglades,' she said petulantly. 'They're about to complete a very extensive study that will prove that.'

He sighed noisily. 'The study was published a month ago, and what it proved was that the water-management programme—the very programme designed to protect the 'Glades—is killing it, acre by acre, year by year. Certain people would like that information kept quiet, or, at the very least, discredited.'

Melanie stopped dead and looked up at him, blue eyes quiet. 'I didn't read anything about the water-management programme hurting the Everglades...'

He turned and continued walking. 'Then you'd better do a little more reading.'

Melanie trotted to catch up with him, plucking at his arm like a child trying to get the attention of an adult. 'But I read everything Beau gave me...'

'Then he didn't give you everything.'

She scowled at the ground as she walked, wondering why Beau wouldn't have included such a vital study in the reading he gave her, and then finally her face cleared when the answer came to her. It was so obvious that she felt foolish for not realising it immediately. Beau hadn't read the study either; he probably didn't even have it.

'I'll get a copy of that study and read it just as soon as I get back to Tallahassee,' she said firmly.

'You can read it tonight. I've got a copy at the cabin.'

'Good. And, if what you say is true, I know Beau will work as hard as anyone against cutting the budget.'

'Oh, wonderful. I feel much better now.'

Melanie stopped walking and glared at him. 'He will,' she insisted, her lower lip creeping out a fraction. 'And if you doubt that, it's only because you don't know him.'

'And you do?' He stopped and turned to face her.

'Of course I do,' she said, trying to keep the doubt out of her voice. The truth was, she'd been shaken to learn the real reason Beau had wanted her to come here; it had made her wonder if she really knew the man she was going to marry at all. 'He's a good and honourable man, and I'm sure he thinks he's doing the right thing...' She recited the words as if they were a chant that would make them true.

Cage snorted derisively. 'If he's so sure voting to cut the Everglades budget is the right thing to do, why did he even bother going through the motions of sending someone down here?'

Melanie hesitated. 'He's...afraid of you. Afraid you could use your money and power to convince the voters he *wasn't* right, even if he was.'

Cage gave her a long-suffering look. 'If it were really the right thing to do, the facts would support him, and no one—not even me—could convince the voters otherwise.'

Melanie looked down and frowned hard at the strange, ugly boots on her feet.

'There is no honour without honesty, Melanie.'

Her head jerked up with a small remnant of her old defiance. 'I know that.'

'Parker hasn't been honest with any of us—not the voters, not me, not even you—so what is it that makes you think he's such an honourable man?'

Melanie sighed and bit down on her lip, trying to sort out the jumble of her thoughts.

'Were you supposed to sleep with me? Was that my consolation prize?'

She flinched hard, shifting her hair from her shoulders to tumble down her back. 'Dear lord, no!' she gasped. 'Is *that* what you think...?'

He shrugged idly. 'What am I supposed to think? I invite a congressman, and who does he send as his representative? An aide? A well-informed, experienced professional? No. He sends a woman who's never seen the Everglades; who's afraid of everything in them; a woman who doesn't know the first thing about a fact-finding expedition, but who sure as hell could make any man forget what he was trying to accomplish in the first place.'

Melanie just stared at him. She'd heard everything he said, but her mind had zeroed in on the last part and wouldn't let go.

'Weren't you a little suspicious yourself when you found out the trip was a ruse?' he asked innocently. 'Didn't you wonder just what it was you were supposed to do to pacify me?'

Her mouth quivered uncertainly. 'You don't understand. It wasn't like that. He told me to use some of my Southern charm...'

One side of his mouth moved slightly, and he arched one brow. 'Right.'

'And he meant *charm*,' she insisted, frowning now. 'Nothing else. Beau doesn't even *think* of me that way...'

'There isn't a man alive who could help but think of you that way.'

Her breath caught in her throat, and she had to swallow before she could continue. 'Southern gentlemen do not think of the future mothers of their children like that——' she started to say, and once again he interrupted her, leaving her with her lips parted and her thought barely begun.

'Who the hell told you that?'

Melanie swallowed hard, confused by the sudden twist in the conversation.

'Good lord,' Cage said quietly. 'That's why you think he's such a "good and honourable man", isn't it? Because he hasn't taken you yet.'

Her peripheral vision caught the motion of the canteens as he let them slide from his arms, but she was afraid to take her eyes from his, even when she felt his hands close around her upper arms. 'Hell, Melanie; haven't you wondered if there just wasn't something missing that was supposed to be there?'

She stilled under his hands, shocked to hear the thought that had troubled her most spoken aloud.

He looked deeply into her eyes, then frowned in genuine puzzlement. 'Why?' he whispered. 'Why would you choose a man like that?'

With that single question, all the tidy pieces of her life seemed to explode outward, and that train she'd always felt as if she were riding screeched to a halt, dropping her in the middle of nowhere, leaving her to find her own way. She hadn't really *chosen* Beau, any more than she'd chosen anything else in her life. He'd been...provided. 'I've arranged for you to meet a special man tonight, Mellie,' her father had said, 'the perfect man; the kind of man your mother and I always dreamed our baby girl would marry.'

'Why?' Cage was repeating again, and she became aware of his hands tightening on her arms. She blinked her way out of her confused thoughts, and for the first time saw the dark tightness of desire on a man's face.

'Honour and honesty,' he said, barely moving his lips, the total focus of his intention spearing her from the black centres of his eyes. 'They're inseparable. Seeing you and not wanting you is dishonest. Touching you...' his thumbs stroked through the fabric of her sleeves along the insides of her arms, making her shiver '...and not taking you is dishonest.'

With the sudden, thoughtless instinct of prey recognising predator, she started to scramble backwards—not necessarily because it was what she wanted to do, but because it was the only reaction that seemed proper.

'Oh, no, you don't,' he murmured, pulling her against his chest, one broad hand solid on her back, the other circling her neck with a thumb under her chin, holding her head still.

'Cage, no,' she whispered, feeling a rapid hammering against her chest that might have been her heartbeat or his. 'You can't do this. You have to let me go.' She searched his face for a remnant of reason, but all she saw was an intensity of purpose that narrowed the dark eyes and drew lines of determination at the corners.

'I'll make a deal with you,' he said in a voice so harsh that she barely recognised it as his. 'If you ask me to let you go again, I will.'

The statement so puzzled her that she was totally unprepared for the sudden, hard descent of his mouth on hers. She went rigid against the brace of his arm, feeling her lips flattened against her teeth. The first thought to leap into her mind was that she wasn't being kissed; she was being conquered. The next thought was that Benjamin Cage tasted exactly the way he smelled—tangy and sweet and musky and wild, and very, very hot. As his fingers twined into her hair, pulling her head back, his mouth worked against hers expertly, making it strangely hard to draw breath.

It's the heat, she thought crazily. You simply can't breathe properly in this kind of weather. But then she felt the slick wetness of his tongue at the crease of her lips, and knew that the steaming liquid rush she felt in the pit of her stomach had nothing to do with external temperatures.

Nothing in her life had prepared her for this singular moment when she would feel physical desire for the first time. No one had taught her that it should be resisted, that there was merit in exercising control over the frantic demands of her own body—perhaps because no one had ever imagined that a well-bred, well-raised daughter of the South would ever feel such things.

As they stood staring into each other's eyes, his hands slid down the generous rise of her breasts, opening the buttons of her overshirt along the way. He parted the shirt and looked down at the sharp outline of her nipples against the thin cloth of the T-shirt, and, just when she was sure she could feel his gaze as strongly as she would have felt his hand, he touched a forefinger lightly to one shuddering peak and her knees threatened to buckle.

It was totally unlike the forceful, hasty press of Beau's hands on those occasions when he'd done more than kiss her. Once, and only once, she'd grabbed his hand and held it to her breast, thinking that if the moment could be prolonged it would eventually mature into tenderness. He'd pulled back immediately, obviously disconcerted that the proper young woman he was going to marry was capable of such boldness. She'd seen the disappointment, maybe even the wariness in his face, and knew instinctively that taking the initiative had threatened him somehow. He'd made her feel like a whore with that single glance, and she'd been passive ever since.

But passiveness now was impossible, and blessedly unnecessary. At Cage's touch she'd grabbed his arms to hold herself erect, and the convulsive leap of his biceps beneath her fingers told her that here was a man who responded to passion, not submission.

She felt as if bonds that had chafed her spirit for a lifetime had been suddenly cut, granting her a freedom she'd never known existed. For this gift alone, she knew she would love Benjamin Cage forever, and the last remnant of the woman everyone thought she was and should be disappeared forever. She gazed up at Cage with clear, shining eyes, and showed him the heart that had been hiding there.

There was an almost imperceptible narrowing of his eyes, as if she'd uttered something profound, and for a moment, his hands stilled on her breasts. Then his lips moved silently to form her name and his hands moved to her shoulders. He pushed the straps of her sleeveless T-shirt and her shirt down to her elbows, effectively pinning her arms, exposing her breasts. They seemed to rise towards him with her startled intake of breath. He stared at them, then released a long, shaky exhalation and let his eyes fall closed. Melanie saw the frantic beat of the pulse in his corded neck, felt the trembling of his hands on her arms, and then suddenly he was looking down at her again, his eyes wide and clear and perfectly eloquent, as if an-

nouncing his intentions. When he reached out to fill
his hands with her breasts, when thumbs and fore-
fingers found her nipples and began to massage gently,
her own eyes fell closed and she sank helplessly to her
knees.

Following her down, he let his mouth find her neck,
then her collar-bone, and finally his lips closed around
the peak of her left breast. She moaned aloud, her
back arching, and then she felt tongue and teeth
tasting delicately at first, then sucking hard as her head
fell back on her shoulders. She reached for the back
of his head, whimpering when the prison of her own
clothes frustrated her. He sat back on his haunches
and tore the shirt from her arms, then rested there a
moment, breathing through his mouth, black hair
dangling over eyes hooded to gaze into hers.

'I've always taken what I wanted from life, and
made it mine.' He exhaled raggedly, then paused to
take a series of shaky breaths. 'But I've never wanted
anything so much.'

She didn't know if those were really the words she'd
always wanted to hear from a man. She only knew
that they made her feel like a woman for perhaps the
first time in her life. It didn't matter that he hadn't
mentioned love, because love and desire had to be
part of the same thing, or else the whole world was
upside-down.

When she reached for him, not wanting him to talk,
not wanting words that would remind her of that other
world and promises she had made there, he snatched
her wrists and held them, his eyes fierce. She met his
gaze fully, her eyes darkened by forest and passion to
a deeper, more complex blue, then she slowly drew
his hand back to her breast.

A brief shudder passed through him as he took her by the shoulders and lowered her gently to the forest floor. As his mouth travelled over her face and neck his hand loosened the waistband of the heavy canvas trousers, then slid beneath her lace panties to rest lightly on the softness of her stomach. She gasped quietly at his touch, then felt a great, peaceful stillness settle over her body, a powerful sense of certainty which she wanted to last for the rest of her life. This was what she wanted. *He* was what she wanted. Forever.

Trembling beneath him, clutching the back of his head, she felt his fingers slip down her stomach into the damp forest of hair, then further into the slick wetness of passion that throbbed under his touch. Her back arched involuntarily and she whimpered as he cupped her gently, then allowed his fingers to travel in tender exploration.

She was vaguely aware of the leafy canopy overhead, of filtered sunlight dappling her face. Her hair spread in a golden fan on the rich brown soil, and occasionally, when a leaf stirred above, a shard of sunlight found a lighter strand of blonde and seemed to set it on fire. In some distant part of her mind, Melanie savoured the sweet irony of first being touched by a man in a savagely beautiful wilderness as pristine and innocent of man's touch as she was.

Cage's dark eyes drank in the sight of her face as his hands caressed her, and Melanie was gazing up at him in wonderment when suddenly his eyes flickered, then froze on a point just past her head. She opened her mouth to speak, but he silenced her with a quick, urgent tightening of his eyes. Completely silent, his lips mouthed the words, 'Don't move.'

Less than a hand's breadth from the top of Melanie's head, Cage's gaze was fixed on a blunt, cylindrical head poised over the fan of blonde blocking its path, its dark tongue flicking curiously.

His breath caught in his throat, his body painfully rigid, Cage tried to keep the horror out of his eyes as the small, deadly snake wove its black and yellow and red body through the blonde strands.

Beneath him, Melanie lay perfectly still, watching his eyes track slowly to the left. His fear was almost palpable, and she sensed the rigid tension of muscles prepared to react instantly and violently. She felt the soft stir of something moving in her hair, and when she saw his nostrils flare and his gaze sharpen, she knew instinctively that her life depended on remaining motionless. And yet miraculously—foolishly, perhaps—she was not afraid. Cage would never let anything hurt her. She knew that with a greater certainty than she had ever known anything in her life.

She watched as his eyes tracked so far to the left that a great portion of the whites showed; and then slowly, with a shudder that passed violently through his entire body, his lids fell closed in relief.

In one quick, fluid motion he slipped his hand from her pants, gathered his legs beneath him and rose to his feet, pulling her with him. His embrace was so fierce that it was painful.

'Dear lord,' he breathed raggedly into her ear, his voice as tight as the arms that held her.

She leaned back against his arm and looked up at him. His face was twisted, tortured by thoughts of what might have been. 'What was it?' she whispered.

He swallowed hard. 'Snake,' was all he could manage to utter.

'I thought so.'

His eyes widened. 'You thought so?' he repeated numbly, and she nodded.

'I felt something in my hair, and I saw you staring, watching it move along the ground...it couldn't have been anything else.'

He shook his head as if to clear it, mystified by her reaction. 'But you're terrified of snakes. You fainted when you *saw* one...'

'I know. But I wasn't afraid this time. This time I knew you wouldn't let anything hurt me.'

He stared at her in dull disbelief for a moment, then his face darkened in anger she didn't understand. 'Dammit, it was a *coral* snake, Melanie. They're deadly. They make the cottonmouth seem like a household pet. One bite and...' His voice caught and he shuddered.

'I'm sorry,' she murmured, wanting to erase the anger from his face; wanting to make everything all right again.

'You're sorry,' he echoed dully. 'I let things get out of hand and nearly get you killed, and you're sorry.' He turned his head away, frowning hard, then took his hands from her and jammed them in his pockets. She started to lift her hand to reach for his arm, then looked at his face and knew that something was suddenly, terribly wrong. She let her hand fall back to her side. The crease between his brows had deepened with the intensity of his thoughts, and the muscle along his jaw stood out in sharp relief. He's going away, she thought, without realising where the thought had come from; but still her gaze remained riveted to his face, as if her whole future hung in the balance. She was afraid to speak.

Finally he released a long, sombre sigh and turned his head to look straight at her. 'This was all wrong. We're probably lucky that snake came along when it did.'

Melanie felt her heart still in her chest, and she had to concentrate fiercely to keep her voice steady. 'Why was it all wrong?'

His brows twitched once in a pained expression. It was the last visible sign of emotion he would give her. 'Because you want more than I can give you.'

She felt a prickle crawling up her spine, that prelude to an adrenalin surge the body sensed long before the mind directed the legs to run. 'I don't understand,' she whispered.

There was no more black fire in his eyes. The surfaces looked flat and impenetrable. 'You wanted love, and I can't give you that.'

She could sense her chest rising and falling, so she knew she was breathing, but she wondered how she could manage that with her heart lying so dead and still. 'But . . . we almost made love . . .'

'No. We almost had sex. I don't think you know what love is yet.'

She flinched at each word as if it were a blow, standing there stoically like a torture victim determined not to show pain. He didn't love her? What they'd felt together; what they'd shared together— that hadn't been love? After a time it occurred to her that she should say something. 'Really,' was all she could manage to utter, and for some reason that response seemed to amuse him. She felt the sharp, ironic twist of his mouth like a knife in her stomach.

'You would have hated yourself later, you know. Once you came to your senses and went back where you belong.'

Her eyes fell painfully closed at the 'came to your senses' remark. It made her sound the way . . . the way Beau had made her feel that one time she'd held his hand to her breast. Melanie the Wanton, she thought with a grim smile that never made it from her mind to her lips.

'You should cover yourself.' He was staring at her bare breasts, and, when she realised that, she felt the stirrings of shame where a moment before there had been none. It had been all right as long as he'd been holding her; as long as she'd been within the circle of his arms and his tender attention. But now she was just a half-naked woman being told to cover herself.

Her face started to colour slowly, as if humiliation was an afterthought—something she just remembered she was supposed to feel. It felt the same as it had all those years before when an appalled nanny had chased her naked across the lawn. She pushed arms she could barely feel through the straps of her T-shirt and pulled it up over her shoulders, keeping her eyes cast down. It wasn't necessary to see his face to feel the indifference of his gaze, and it was all she could do to keep her features rigidly aligned; to pretend it didn't matter; to maintain that level of control the human animal clung to as a shield against despair.

You can live through this, Melanie, she tried to tell herself. It isn't the end of the world, just because the first man you've ever wanted—the first man you've ever loved—doesn't want you . . .

She heard his voice like a pain coursing through every nerve. Dear lord, she thought, I'm falling apart at the sound of his voice; what will happen if I look at him again?

'Melanie?' he repeated. 'I asked if you wanted to go back.'

'Back?' she asked with forced lightness, hurriedly pulling on the shirt. 'Back where? To the cabin? To Tallahassee? Or all the way back home to Georgia?'

He was quiet for a time, and she felt his stare as she looked down, pretending to concentrate on her buttons. 'Wherever.'

She took a deep breath and looked around, anywhere but at him.

'Look at me, Melanie.'

And there it was. The command to bare soul and mind through the windows of her eyes. The insistence that she look again on what she couldn't have, and show her pain.

She turned her head very slowly and gazed upon the sheer masculine beauty of his face, her own features perfectly composed. 'What is it?' she asked calmly.

He didn't see the agony the gesture had cost her; he couldn't see that she wanted to double over with the pain of something absolutely essential being torn from deep inside. 'Do you want to go back?' he repeated.

'No,' she said firmly. She wasn't going back. Not empty-handed. If she couldn't have Benjamin Cage, the very least she was taking out of this miserable sticky place was a piece of her own family history. 'I want to meet the Seminole woman. I want to hear the legend. You promised me that.'

He was silent for what seemed like a very long time, and in the silence they stared at each other, proud blue eyes and proud brown ones each jealously guarding the private thoughts behind them.

'Let's go,' Cage said finally, turning and striding deeper into the forest that was part of his world, and as alien to Melanie as the far side of the moon.

It occurred to her as she followed him how much he belonged here, and how much she didn't. Hadn't she been foolish to imagine an affinity with such a man? They weren't the least bit alike...

In the distance she heard the mournful shriek of some wild, exotic bird, and thought it sounded like a woman screaming.

CHAPTER EIGHT

FOR the better part of an hour Cage paddled the oddly short aluminium canoe through a labyrinth of serpentine waterways. Melanie sat on the front bench, resisting the urge to look back at him. She barely noticed the green, brackish water slipping beneath the hull, the riotous colour of jumbo orchids peeking through the deeply shaded jungle around them, or even the feathery strands of moss dangling from overhead branches, sometimes brushing against her face like the dainty webs of spiders. She was too busy wrestling with her emotions, remembering what had happened between them back on the forest floor, and trying to forget what had been said afterwards.

Forever. That was what she had decided back there—that Cage was what she wanted for the rest of her life. That was love, wasn't it? But what did love become when it wasn't returned? Could it even exist at all?

She worried the questions in troubled silence, unaware of Cage's eyes on her from the back, flickering with something like pain whenever she lifted her head or moved her shoulders in a sigh.

After a time he spoke occasionally, but only to point out an unusual plant or bird, or to call her attention to once-lush areas now drained dry by the canals and choked with brush. It was doubly painful that he could speak so calmly of such inconsequential things, as if nothing at all had happened between them. Very little

122

of what he said registered, but she felt the sound of his voice through every nerve in her body.

'There used to be thousands of snowy egrets nesting right here,' he said at one point. 'Now the water is gone, the fish are gone, and the egrets are gone, too. That's our water-management system for you.'

Her only response was to nod absently as she rubbed at her arms, trying to erase the memory of the way his hands had felt on her skin.

At times the watery road they followed seemed to disappear in a thick jumble of floating lilies, but Cage just continued to paddle through the viney mass, always finding a clear passage beyond.

Eventually he steered the canoe into a part of the bank that looked exactly like every other part, and tossed a line over an overhanging branch. 'We're here,' he said perfunctorily, extending a hand to help her on to the reedy shore.

Melanie clung to his hand until he pulled away and pushed through the undergrowth to a hidden path. Without a backward glance to make sure she could follow through grasses and ferns taller than she was, he stomped ahead into a stand of old-growth mahogany. For the first time in well over an hour she felt the edge of her pain sharpen into resentment.

Beau would never do that, she thought bitterly, hurrying to keep Cage in sight. Beau would never push on ahead and leave me to find my own way. He'd be right back here next to me, one hand on my elbow, eyes watchful to make sure I didn't step wrong. And, come to think of it, Beau wouldn't expect me to use an outhouse, either, or to shower outside or tie up a boat or trudge through a forest in a hundred-degree heat. He wouldn't even think of asking such things.

He knows the limits of my experience, and doesn't fault me for it. Cage, damn him anyway, doesn't think I *have* any limits.

She froze suddenly, feeling as if she'd been hit in the stomach with a two-by-four, blinking at the sudden, faint glimmer of understanding that was almost like a visible spark in the air ahead. Her mind reached out, grasping for that elusive spark like a child chasing fireflies in the dark.

'Melanie, dammit! Hurry up!'

She jumped at Cage's impatient shout from somewhere up the trail, frustrated by the distraction. The bright glimmer her thoughts had been chasing seemed to disperse into a million pinpricks of light, and she cursed softly under her breath and trudged forward.

She found Cage a short distance ahead, looking up at a small palm-thatched hut rising amid the trees. A rickety flight of steps rose upward to what seemed little more than a roofed platform—no screens, no walls, just woven mats partially rolled up to admit the slightest breeze. 'There it is,' he said.

'Someone actually lives here?'

A figure suddenly appeared at the top of the steps. 'She does.'

As she drew close enough to see the woman clearly Melanie caught herself staring in disbelief. It seemed impossible that anyone who looked that old could even draw breath, let alone exude the vitality this woman did without moving a muscle. She was incredibly tall, thin, and totally without the stoop Melanie had come to expect from people of a great age. Her skin was nut-brown and deeply seamed; her full, brightly coloured skirt brushed her ankles, and a blazing red bandana was wrapped so tightly around her skull that Melanie wondered if she had any hair beneath it. 'Hurry up!' she called down to Cage in a strong, youthful voice, and he left Melanie behind, vaulting up the stairs to lift the old Seminole woman in an exuberant embrace.

Melanie gazed up at the pair, feeling for an old, barefoot Seminole woman one of the first pangs of envy she'd ever felt in her life. Cage's love for the old woman seemed to radiate like a miniature sun—she saw it in the way he held her, heard it in the mellow music of his laughter—and realised with a wrenching pain that, whatever Cage had felt for her back on that forest trail, it had not filled him with this kind of joy.

She dropped her eyes abruptly, feeling like an unwelcome intruder.

'Come up, Melanie.' His voice drifted down like early morning mist in the sudden silence.

She climbed reluctantly, her boots thumping noisily on the risers, as out of place on her feet as she was in the Everglades. She should never have come here, she thought as she climbed. She didn't belong here. Not in Cage's beloved swamp; not in this old woman's pathetic hut...

And then suddenly she was at the top of the stairs and the old woman turned from Cage and looked at her, and Melanie almost reeled under the sudden, stunning sense of finally coming home to a place and a face she had never seen before.

It was the woman, of course. She had that rare, magical gift of drawing you into the circle of her warmth with a glance. Perhaps it was simply the serenity of a very old soul; perhaps it was that kind of charisma politicians like Beau could only dream of;

but, whatever it was, Melanie felt herself tremble, humbled by it.

Strong, weathered hands grasped hers and black eyes bright as buttons seemed to peer into her soul. The old face seemed to dissolve in the hundred wrinkles of a smile, and Melanie felt as if the sun had just broken through the clouds to shine on her face. 'You are the first woman Asi has ever brought to me,' the old Seminole woman said quietly. Her voice was rich with the cadenced drawl of the South, her words slow and precise, as if English were her second language.

'It's an honour to meet you,' Melanie murmured, meaning it.

'I think he honours us both. What's your name, child?'

'Melanie.'

The old woman smiled and nodded. 'Call me Grandmother. Everyone does, even this fellow.' She chuckled and poked a bony finger at Cage's arm.

'You're . . . his grandmother?'

'Oh, my, no. He's not nearly lucky enough to have my blood in his veins.' She chuckled again, then tucked Melanie's hand into the crook of her elbow and led her into the full shade of the hut's roof. 'Come along. You, too, Asi. We'll rest while the sun is hot.'

They sat cross-legged in the nearly empty hut, drinking thick, sweet juice from hand-thrown pottery cups with no handles. While the old woman and Cage talked about people with strange names, Melanie absently stroked the woven mat beneath them, strikingly similar to the one on the floor of Cage's cabin.

'You like it?'

Melanie glanced up to find two sets of black eyes on her. 'It's very beautiful.'

The old woman smiled broadly. 'I'll make one for your wedding gift.'

Melanie smiled uncertainly, wondering how she could know about her wedding. She swiped at the damp tendrils clinging to her forehead, then moved her shoulders beneath the hot, heavy mass of her hair, wishing she'd brought a clip.

'I can braid that for you. I used to braid the hair of my daughters, and then my granddaughters, back when the water lapped at the posts below.'

Melanie started to protest automatically.

'Hush.' The old woman moved quickly, pulling a low stool behind Melanie and plunging her fingers into the tangles of her hair. 'This will be much cooler.' She hummed as she started to work, and Melanie felt the muscles in her neck and shoulders start to relax, almost against her will. 'I'm braiding sunlight, Asi,' she heard the old woman say over her head.

Cage smiled briefly. 'I've brought Melanie to hear one of the old legends, Grandmother.'

'Really? Well. I know them all. Which one should I tell?'

There was silence for a moment, then he said quietly, 'Her full name is Melanie Annabelle Brooks.'

The old fingers froze in the intricate weave they were creating, as if they had suddenly become part of it. Melanie thought she felt them tremble slightly.

'She wants to hear the legend about her great-great-great-grandmother,' Cage added.

After what seemed like a very long time the old woman sighed, as if she'd been holding her breath. Melanie imagined she could feel the whisper of that sigh pass through her hair to tickle her scalp. 'Is this true, child? Melanie Annabelle Brooks was your ancestor?'

Melanie nodded, puzzled by the crackle of tension in the air.

'How did you find her, Asi?' the old woman whispered.

'Actually, she found me.'

Melanie heard another sigh from behind her, this one almost musical. After what seemed like a very long time the fingers started their work again.

'All right, then.' The old woman cleared her throat and began to recite. 'Truth and legend weave together, like the mat we sit on, like the braid of your hair, and so this is the legend, and this is the truth.' Melanie felt the shivery thrill of a child hearing her first ghost story by an open camp-fire. Cage straightened slightly opposite her, fixing her with his eyes as they both listened.

'Once there was a young warrior who rode at the right side of Osceola, the greatest Seminole warrior of all. On a raid in a place called Creek County, the young warrior was wounded and separated from his band. He hid himself in a great forest, and there he saw a woman sitting on the bank of a creek. She had hair the colour of the sun... like yours, child... and the young warrior was blinded by her beauty. He remained hidden, watching her, until a doe and her fawn came to drink at the creek, and the woman became a tree...'

'She means she didn't move,' Cage interrupted, and the old woman clucked her tongue impatiently.

'She knows that,' she said sharply. 'There is a good mind beneath all this hair. I can see it.'

Cage looked down, properly chastised, but Melanie could see him suppressing a smile.

'The woman was so moved by the beauty of the deer that tears fell from her eyes, and the warrior knew then that her heart was good. He showed himself and they talked with their eyes, and fell in love before the first words were spoken.'

Melanie saw the story come to life in her mind, imagining a dark man with eyes like Cage first startling, then entrancing a young woman who had heard eloquence, but never seen it in a man's face.

'She took the warrior to a secret place to tend his wounds and kept him hidden from all eyes but hers. For the time it took him to heal they loved only with their eyes and hearts, because he was an Indian warrior and she was a great white man's wife, and only their spirits could join. And then one day she disappeared, and her husband thought she was dead, but she was only bringing her warrior home.'

The old woman paused a moment. 'Her name was Melanie Annabelle Brooks, and she stayed with the Seminole many days, learning the ways of the tribe and this place. The warrior's parents called her daughter, honouring her for saving the life of their son. Others called her the White Seminole. On the day she left to return to her home they say the sky looked down on the warrior and the white woman and wept, because you could see their hearts breaking in their eyes.'

Melanie felt the old hands drop from her hair, but remained motionless, connected to a woman who had died more than a century before; a woman who had also found love here in the Everglades, a love she couldn't keep.

Finally she reached up to wipe her cheeks with both hands, unashamed of her tears. Cage was looking at her, his lips pressed tightly together.

'That is your legend, child,' the old woman murmured.

Melanie turned to look at her, her eyes brimming again. A gnarled hand cupped her chin while the other wiped gently at her cheeks.

'You shouldn't cry,' she smiled tenderly. 'This is a great day. The circle is closing.'

'What do you mean?' Melanie sniffed.

The old woman's eyes speared Cage. 'Asi?'

'Why do you call him that?'

'Because it's his name.'

Cage scowled at her questioning glance, then grumbled, 'My full name is Benjamin Osceola Cage.'

'Benjamin *Asi-Vaholo* Cage,' the old woman corrected him sternly. 'That is the Seminole name, and that is your name.' She looked at Melanie and smiled. 'The descendants of that young warrior all carry the name of Asi-Vaholo, honouring the memory of that great chief...' Melanie's breath stopped in her throat. 'Asi is the great-great-great-grandson of the young warrior saved by your great-great-great-grandmother.'

Melanie blinked at the old woman, then turned to Cage, her blue eyes round with amazement. 'But this is incredible,' she whispered, wondering why he hadn't told her the legend himself, as soon as he'd found out who she was. She stared at him for a long time, trying to read his expression, then finally looked down at the mat beneath her crossed legs, her mind numb. 'You never said a thing,' she mumbled senselessly. 'I didn't even know you were Seminole...'

The old woman chuckled. 'The generations have diluted his blood, but the spirit is still strong. In his heart, he is Seminole. He carries the spirit of his ancestor, just as you carry the spirit of yours. And now the circle is closing and, in you, the hearts of your ancestors will join at last.'

She rocked back on the little stool, beaming. 'This is a great day. I am grateful I lived to see this day.'

'It's a coincidence, that's all, Grandmother,' Cage said in a voice so flatly indifferent that it made Melanie wince. 'Melanie doesn't belong here any more than her ancestor did. The circle is *not* closing.'

The old woman seemed unperturbed. 'You think not? Even you, Asi, are not strong enough to deny destiny. The circle *is* closing, and there's nothing you can do to stop it.'

Suddenly Cage leaped up and stomped from the hut, his feet beating angrily down the primitive stairs outside. The old woman never moved, never glanced after him, and her expression remained serene. 'Men always make such a noise when they're afraid, don't they?' she mused.

Melanie frowned up at her. 'I don't think Cage—Asi—is afraid of anything.'

For some reason that delighted the old woman, and she chuckled deep in her throat. 'He's afraid of you, child; can't you see that?'

Melanie just stared at her.

'You've made him want to love you, and that's a fearful thing for a man afraid to love.'

'Afraid to love?' Melanie echoed in a whisper.

The old woman looked away for a moment, her eyes troubled. 'Perhaps he thinks you will leave, as your ancestor did—as his own mother did. He's afraid to put his love, and therefore his life, in someone else's hands. His father did, and when she left it destroyed him. I think it was then that Asi decided it was easier not to love at all.' She turned back to Melanie with a warm smile, her face creasing like soft, buttery leather. 'I think only women understand that love and pain are also companions, just like truth and legend, and that the joy of one makes the agony of the other bearable. Asi may never be able to let himself love you, but is that really so important? You love him, and that love belongs to you forever. Not even Asi can take that away—unless you let him.'

CHAPTER NINE

THE circle is closing. The phrase repeated itself constantly in Melanie's mind as Cage hurried her back towards the canoe, away from the spartan hut, as if the old woman's ideas about destiny were a disease they might catch if they stayed too long.

Melanie moved mindlessly in the direction she was led, her eyes all but unseeing, her thoughts turned inward. Occasionally she blinked hard, as if the seeds of thought the old woman had planted were as dazzling as the light of the noonday sun.

For the first time Cage seemed uncomfortable with the silence between them. 'Grandmother's getting old,' he grumbled as he pushed the canoe away from the bank. 'Don't put too much stock in what she says. She's too wrapped up in the old legends . . .'

Melanie almost smiled, wondering what he'd think if he knew what had been said after he left the hut. 'You don't believe the legend?'

He shrugged irritably, biting deep into the water with the paddle. 'I believe it happened; but I don't believe that something that happened over a century ago has anything to do with what happens now. Turn around and get your hands inside the boat.'

Melanie jerked her hands to her lap and faced front, her eyes on the silvery prow as it sliced through the murky water. She was still a little shaken by the revelations of the afternoon. It had been surprising enough when Cage had told her her ancestral grand-

133

mother had actually been here; that she had loved Cage's great-great-great-grandfather was one of those unbelievable coincidences that left your sense of logic reeling.

It must have shaken him too, when he first heard my name, she thought, remembering his reaction. At last she understood the things he'd said afterwards, about grand names mandating grand deeds. If that was true, they both had a lot to live up to.

She sighed deeply, watching the impenetrable wall of green slide by the canoe, wondering what it would be like to have the kind of courage her ancestral grandmother had had. She'd sacrificed everything— her reputation, her marriage, even her place in the family history—for love of a man she knew she could never have. No wonder she had become a legend.

Fingering the intricate weave of her hair, she caught herself wondering if the first Melanie Brooks had worn such a braid, and how she could have returned to one man when she loved another.

She pondered that question for a very long time.

The sun had barely dipped to the treetops when they arrived back at the cabin. As soon as they were inside Cage peeled off his overshirt then sat down on the chair and began taking off his boots. Melanie walked over to sit on the bed, folded her hands in her lap, and watched as he set his boots carefully to one side, then leaned forward, his arms draped across his thighs. 'The old woman fell in love with you.'

Melanie felt her mind smile. At least someone had.

'Part of it was the legend, of course. The Seminole put a lot of stock in legends . . .' He stopped abruptly, frowning at her expression. 'You look . . . different.' His black hair shifted slightly as he tipped his head.

'Do I? It must be the braid.'

He shook his head, dark eyes fixed on hers, his expression suddenly still, as if he were catching a mental breath. Melanie used the moment to memorise that exotic, implacable face with its stoic gaze and carved features, making a photograph her mind would carry with her forever.

Suddenly he looked down, breaking eye-contact, then braced his hands on his knees and stood. 'I'd better get us something to eat. It's going to be full dark soon. You light the lamps.'

She remained sitting for a moment, looking out at the deepening shadows of dusk with a faint, rueful smile. He actually thought she'd been paying attention when he showed her how to light the lamps. He actually expected her to do that without any help, just as he'd expected her to use an outdoor shower and tie a boat and keep pace with those impossibly long strides of his when he stomped through the forest . . . what a testament to fate's sense of mischief that helpless, coddled Melanie Brooks would fall in love with a man who expected more of her than anyone ever had . . .

She tensed on the bed suddenly, feeling her mind snatching at that same firefly glimmer of light she'd sensed on the path to the old woman's hut this morning. But she'd done all those things, hadn't she? She wasn't helpless, coddled Melanie Brooks with Cage, because he expected her to be more than that.

She felt the rush of epiphany like the pulse of wind stirred by a thousand wings. In her mind's eye she saw the bright, blinding essence of her love for Cage and realised it was not so much for the way he made her feel, as the way he made her feel about herself.

'You love him,' the old woman's words echoed in her mind, 'and that love belongs to you forever. Not even Asi can take that away—unless you let him.'

She raised her head and looked across the room to where Cage was busy at the counter, his back to her. Wasn't that what she'd been doing? Ever since the morning she'd been burying her feelings, hiding them like some shameful secret, just because they weren't reciprocated. She wasn't just letting love be taken from her—she was handing it over, like a bloody sacrifice on the altar of her pride.

Her mind felt exquisitely clear, like sunlight on the smooth surface of polished crystal. You may never belong to me, Benjamin Cage; but the love does. The love is mine.

There should have been bells, or fireworks, or a volley of cannon-fire—something to mark this extra-ordinary moment when Melanie Brooks first took her life into her own hands. From cradle to betrothal, everything had been given to her long before she would think to ask for it. It was time—past time—that she learned to take something for herself.

Cage was hunched over the counter lighting the camp stove when she rose quietly from the bed. He swept one hand back through his hair as he straightened. It was beautiful hair, Melanie thought, her hands quietly busy as she watched him from across the room; one of the many gifts of his Seminole heritage. The Indian blood might have been diluted, but the surviving genes were strong. The dark hair and eyes, the classic high cheekbones and the strong, sensual mouth—all these were part of the legacy of his ancestry, as much as his spirit.

When her hands had finished their work she stood rock-still, wondering why she wasn't terrified. She'd been afraid of almost everything all her life—afraid of the dark, afraid of snakes, afraid of making a move without someone telling her what to do—and yet at this moment she was leaping fearlessly into the unknown on the strength of no one's judgement but her own. She could almost feel the whistling rush of wind beneath wings she'd never had.

'Asi,' she murmured, her voice as light as the early evening breeze.

He spun at the sound of that name on her lips, his eyes flashing darkly... and then his mouth dropped open and he took a quick step backwards into the counter.

She was totally naked, the clothing she had so quietly shed lying in a crumpled heap at her bare feet.

She watched his eyes travel the full length of her body and then up to her face again, and for the first time in her life she felt as beautiful as people had always told her she was. Her mouth curved automatically in a smile, and she didn't have to see her reflection to know she had never looked more like her ancestor's portrait than she did at that moment. She'd often wondered at the reason behind that woman's enigmatic smile—even speculated that it might have been a secret, illicit love-affair—but she realised now that it had been more than that. Perhaps consummating a great love wasn't nearly as important as recognising it. Just recognising it was an enormous achievement. And it made you smile.

The smile deepened as she watched Benjamin's face darken and his throat move convulsively. She felt wonderfully strong, almost invincible; a feeling so alien that she marvelled that it was hers. Maybe it isn't, she mused. Maybe I've been possessed by that part of the first Melanie Brooks's spirit that still lingers here, in the Everglades—or maybe a part of that spirit was alive in me all the time, and I just never knew it.

'What the hell do you think you're doing?' he rasped.

She met his gaze fully, but felt her lower lip threaten to quiver. She'd never seduced a man before, and she didn't quite know what to do next. 'I'm ... finishing what we started this morning.'

His eyes narrowed sharply and suddenly without losing their focus on hers, and Melanie imagined that she saw deep within them a reflection of that fear the old woman had talked about. Fear of love, of trusting, of commitment.

'You don't have to love me,' she tried to reassure him, hoping he wouldn't notice how the words caught in her throat. 'I don't expect that. This isn't forever. It's just for now.'

In the deep silence that followed, while Cage stared harshly, almost hatefully into her eyes, she started to wonder what she would do if he simply turned his back on her ...

She needn't have worried. In the next instant a strangled sound rose from his throat, and he moved so quickly that she barely saw him cover the distance between them. One second he was across the room; the next he was kneeling at her feet, his arms around her bare hips, his mouth pressed into her stomach as if to seal his voice inside.

She looked down at the tangle of his hair, violently black against the white of her skin, and plunged her fingers into it, pulling him against her. At the silken touch of his tongue she sagged forward, and just when she thought her knees would collapse he rose to his feet, gathered her in his arms and laid her on the bed.

Standing over her, his eyes black and seething, he growled, 'I'll give you one last chance to think about what you're doing. Whatever your reasons, when you get back where you belong they aren't going to seem good enough.' He remained motionless next to the bed, only the crackle of his eyes and the strained lines around his mouth revealing emotion barely kept in check.

Melanie gazed up at him, blue eyes perfectly still, perfectly sad. How strange that he could wonder at her reasons, when she felt they must be shining from her eyes, as easily read as a neon sign flashing against a dark sky. Couldn't he see that for her, at least, making love was only the confirmation of loving? She wanted desperately to give her heart a voice, to be as unafraid to state her feelings aloud as she was to express them with her body... but the old woman had told the truth. Cage *was* afraid of love—he'd said as much this morning when he'd told her she'd wanted more than he could give. And, if he knew now that what she really wanted was forever, he might not let her have the single moment she was willing to settle for.

It was better, she thought, to say nothing at all. She lifted her arms and parted her lips and invited him home.

In the next few moments she forgot that he didn't love her, because such a thing seemed impossible. How could his touch and his eyes and his voice be so gentle, so cherishing, without love behind them? How could his breath come as rapidly as hers; his heart pound as frantically as his lips and tongue and hands explored her body and left a trail of fire?

Blue eyes dark and wide, she watched breathlessly as he straightened and stripped out of his clothes, then she held up one hand. 'Wait,' she said, her voice husky. 'I want to look at you.'

Surprise flickered across his dark face, but he stood obediently, proudly naked as she studied his body. Astonished innocence and fiery passion mingled in her face in an extraordinary combination. She reached out tentatively to let her fingers flutter over the hard muscles of his thigh, then up to tremble across the ridges of his stomach. Wonderfully intricate musculature convulsed under her hand as she stroked downwards, and she looked up at his face with a tiny, awestruck smile.

It was his face, more than the velvet beat now encased in her hand, that startled her with a molten rush that seemed to tug painfully from within.

'Melanie,' he murmured, coming down on her slowly, hesitantly, the bed reflecting the violent trembling of his restraint. The black fire of his eyes met the blue fire of hers as he braced himself over her, and in spite of the savage fierceness in his expression she knew that this last searching look was a question, a final offer for her to say no before it was too late. She loved him even more for that last supreme gift of choice, and thanked him by lifting her hips to meet his.

'Asi,' she breathed into his ear, because no other name could have belonged to him in this moment, when, whether he wanted it or not, the circle finally closed.

*   *   *

When Melanie awoke, the cabin was already shimmering in the diffused golden light of early morning. Outside, she could hear the raspy night music of insects just giving way to the sunrise chatter of birds.

She rolled on her side in the empty bed, expecting to see Cage somewhere in the cabin, then sat up with a start to find herself totally alone. 'Benjamin?' she whispered, a formless fear tightening in her stomach.

A hundred times during the night she'd wondered what the morning would bring; how Benjamin would relate to her in the cold light of day, after all that hot, passionate melding in the dark. Would he be tender? Cool? Or, heaven forbid, would he make light of it and suggest that they be friends? She hadn't known what to expect, but what she had expected least was to wake up and find him gone altogether.

Straining to sort out all the sounds of the Everglades coming to life, she finally heard the distant splash of the makeshift shower under the porch. Strangely relieved, she propped the pillow against the wall and sat up, tugging the sheet up over her breasts.

At the sound of the screen door her breath seemed to freeze in her throat and her heart turned over in her chest. She turned her head to look at him, and it felt as if all her emotions had suddenly raced to gather in her eyes, making them a liquid blue stream that could cross the room and touch him. 'Good morning,' she whispered.

He stood in the filtered sun of the doorway, jeans-clad legs spread, his bronzed chest and arms sparkling with jewels of water. A white towel dangled forgotten from his hand as he remained motionless, gazing across the room at her, as if he didn't know what to do next. 'Good morning,' he finally replied.

Melanie stared at him for an endless moment, praying he would cross the room and gather her up in his arms and end this terrible awkwardness between them, but he didn't move; he just continued to stand there, looking at her.

'How do you feel?' he asked.

Her mouth twitched in a poor excuse for a smile. 'Fine. I'm just fine.' Oh, hell. This was awful. They were making that dreadful kind of small talk people made when they met acquaintances on the street. Was this the way it was going to be? Were they just going to pretend that last night had never happened?

'No regrets?'

Her eyes flickered at that. 'None.'

The muscle in his jaw tightened briefly, then he dropped his eyes and frowned at the towel in his hand as if he couldn't remember how it had got there.

'When are you going home?' he asked without looking up.

She tensed under the sheet, wounded by his obvious eagerness to be rid of her. 'The plane comes for me tomorrow morning.' Unless you ask me to stay, she added to herself. That's all you'd have to do. Just ask. Please ask...

He nodded briskly, sending a cascade of water droplets flying from the thick, wet tousle of black hair that made him look almost boyish. 'Do you still intend to make a report to the congressman?'

Melanie frowned in momentary confusion. She'd almost forgotten what she'd come here to do, and that he should bring it up so quickly on the heels of last night seemed to negate everything that had happened between them—but that was what he wanted, she realised. 'Yes,' she managed to force out. 'I suppose...'

'Fine. Then there's still a lot you have to see. We should get started.'

She blinked at him, shaken by the chill in his voice and his manner. She held her breath, as if that would help hold all her emotions inside, too. You asked for it, she reminded herself. You knew that he couldn't give you love, and it didn't make any difference. All you wanted was a chance to give him yours. So what did you expect? Were you really harbouring some tiny, pathetic spark of hope that making love would make love happen?

She took a deep breath and licked her lips. 'I'd like a shower,' she said in a strange, constricted voice, looking down at where her feet made two tiny mountains under the sheet. It was so quiet in the cabin that she could hear the sound of her own breathing, but not her heart. Her heart, she decided, had probably stopped beating.

She didn't know how much time had passed when she heard him speak again. It seemed like an eternity, but when she looked at him he was still standing in exactly the same place, watching her with an animal-like alertness.

'I'll start breakfast,' he said coldly. 'It should be ready by the time you finish your shower.'

It seemed that she had to wait a very long time before he turned and walked over to the counter, giving her the privacy of his back, and then she fumbled for the clothes she'd shed the night before, crumpled into a colourless heap on the floor.

CHAPTER TEN

THIS time Melanie found no childlike pleasure in the primitive open-air shower; no smiling wonder at the bold dragonflies attracted to the spray of water. With impatient swipes of her hand she brushed them away and focused her attention on the mechanics of the business at hand.

She scrubbed herself brutally with the rough cloth, as if heartbreak were just another kind of soil that could be scoured away. The final rinse stung her pinkened, chafed skin, but she almost welcomed the distraction of pain. Even though she wanted to soap her hair, at the last minute her fingers refused to release the band that held the braid. It was her last fragile connection, if not to Cage, at least to the old woman, and, through her, to the first Melanie Brooks. In the end, she simply sprayed it thoroughly and squeezed it dry.

The floral robe was an unwelcome reminder of how light-hearted she had been the last time she'd worn it—she'd felt like a child on an innocent summer adventure then, less than two days ago—but it was all she had to slip on after her shower.

The aroma of sweet fried corncakes met her halfway up the stairs, and she wondered absently how Cage had made the batter without fresh eggs. He was waiting on the porch, holding two plates stacked with crisply browned discs. His gaze swept over her with

studied indifference, flickering slightly when he saw
her braid.

'I'm not very hungry,' she said, pleased that her
voice sounded almost normal. It occurred to her that
she was learning a lot about having the courage to
love against the odds. The real test wasn't in loving
enough to give yourself without hope of return; the
real test was surviving the contempt of others on the
morning after. And, if her ancestor had been able to
survive the contempt of a husband so furious he had
tried to erase her from memory, she could survive this.

'You have to eat something substantial now. We'll
be out in the field all day.' He took a seat, balanced
one plate on his lap and held the other out towards
her.

She sighed and took it reluctantly, sitting in the chair
next to him. He was already dressed, canvas trousers
tucked into the high rubber boots, one of the heavy
shirts open over a black T-shirt. It was demeaning,
somehow, to sit there in robe and bare feet when he
was fully clothed, but she supposed any pretence at
modesty was pretty silly at this point.

'They're here again.'

'Who's here?'

He pointed to the family of green jays they'd
watched yesterday morning. 'Our jays.'

She felt a sudden thrust of pain around her heart,
just because he'd called them 'our jays'. He'd only
meant it as a figure of speech, but it could have been
so much more, and it was the could-have-been that
hurt. Our jays. Two small words that conjured up the
never-to-be image of a lifetime of mornings with Cage
at her side.

'They're noisy things, aren't they?' The overly bright sound of her voice made her wince. Oh, please, please, she thought fervently; let me be strong, just for this one last day. If I have to be so hopelessly in love with a man who can't love me, at least let me keep my heartbreak to myself. A broken heart is such a private thing.

In what seemed to Melanie like a sick parody of companionship, they sat in silence for a time, both pretending interest in the raucous antics of the birds. Cage carved steadily at his stack of corncakes; Melanie merely picked at hers.

'You're not eating.'

She forced a small bite into her mouth, chewed, and swallowed. 'I told you I wasn't very hungry.'

He sighed audibly, and when he spoke again his voice was strained. 'We can't go through the whole day like this, Melanie. We have to talk about last night.'

She exhaled sharply in a wry, silent laugh. 'What is there to say about last night?'

'That it was wrong. That I shouldn't have let it happen.'

Her lower lip started to quiver, but she caught it before it became visible. 'You didn't let anything happen. I made it happen. It was my choice, not yours.'

'I didn't expect you to choose sex without love,' he said caustically. 'I didn't expect you to settle for that.'

Melanie turned her head slowly to look at him. Contempt was a funny thing, she was beginning to realise. It only hurt if you accepted it; if you thought you deserved it; and she didn't. She'd given herself out of love, and there was no shame in that.

'I don't regret it,' she said with quiet defiance. 'I don't regret a minute of it.'

'I don't regret it either,' he snapped, glaring at her, the muscle in his jaw standing out in sharp relief. 'I just wish...' he hesitated for a moment while something like a pained expression flickered across his face '...I just wish there could have been more between us.'

Oh, lord. She didn't know which was worse, his contempt, or his pity. Now he was apologising for not loving her. 'So do I,' she replied dully, staring off into the greenery, seeing nothing.

Oddly enough, as strained as the conversation had been, things seemed easier between them afterwards, as if having it all out in the open had relieved them both of the responsibility of their actions.

Cage seemed distant as he told her what he intended to show her on her last day, but then he had been distant from the beginning—until yesterday. As a matter of fact, she thought sadly, looking at the two of them now, you might think that yesterday had never happened at all; that she and Cage were simply two people who didn't know each other very well, a little uncomfortable with each other.

Men were basically a mystery, she decided as she was dressing in the ugly trousers and shirt. They were obviously capable of separating sex from love for their own purposes, and yet they thought less of a woman who was willing to accept them on those terms. What kind of sense did that make?

She stole a glance at Cage over at the counter, clearing up the breakfast dishes, and wondered if she would ever be able to look at him without feeling that painful tightening in her chest. This is pay day, she thought miserably; fate finally balancing the scales, exacting a payment for the fairy-tale life you've had so far.

They started her final tour in the canoe, although Cage had told her they'd ultimately end up in the airboat. Melanie felt even more useless than usual, sitting in front while Cage paddled from the stern. That was another thing she'd never done. Good lord. She was twenty-four years old, and she'd never even paddled a canoe. She was making a mental list of all the things she'd never done for herself, and its length was alarming.

They headed first in the same general direction they'd taken to get to the old woman's cabin yesterday, but veered west at the first discernible fork in the narrow waterway. After a short distance they entered a shadowy mangrove forest whose entire floor was under water, and, to Melanie, every direction looked the same.

'We're taking the long way around to the airboat,' Cage told her as he guided the canoe around aerial roots that lifted the reddish-brown trunks above the waterline. 'If we're lucky we might surprise some woodstorks at a fishing spot I found earlier this year.'

Melanie was gazing up through the spreading branches of glossy, oblong leaves, peppered with pale yellow flowers. 'Why lucky?' she asked absently. 'Is there something special about woodstorks?' She'd seen too many wading birds already to be impressed with any one in particular.

'You never know. On the rare occasions I see them I have to remind myself that I may never see them again. There used to be thousands here, not so many years ago. There are only a few hundred left now.'

'Oh.' A little chagrined, she turned sideways on her bench to look back at him. 'What happened to them? Disease? Poachers . . . ?'

'Preservation,' he replied drily. 'Misguided preservation. One of the many unexpected, unintentional side-effects of the infamous water-management system. Turns out it floods the woodstorks' fishing holes during drydown, letting the fish go too deep for the birds to reach. And like that of most species, their reproduction grinds to a halt when the food supply is gone. They haven't had a proper breeding season in almost a decade. Another year or two of this and the woodstork can take its place next to the dinosaur and the passenger pigeon.'

'I didn't know,' she murmured, troubled by the irony of a conservation effort gone awry, actually destroying the species it had hoped to save.

'It's all in the study you were going to read. You remember the study—the one that's going to make your fiancé fight the budget cut, instead of supporting it?'

She bit her lip in consternation and faced front again, remembering her promise to read the study last night. 'You never gave it to me,' she grumbled.

'I know. I got distracted.'

Her face coloured and she changed the subject quickly. 'I can't see how you know which way to go in here.' She pretended to look around at the watery forest. 'One tree looks just like another.' She heard the paddle lift from the water, spill its drops on the surface, then splash slightly as it entered again.

'See that arch up ahead?' he asked her.

She squinted through the shaded world, finally focusing on a distant arch formed by the branches of two trees coming together. It looked like a doorway to a brighter place.

'It opens on to the sawgrass plain just north of where I keep the airboat. The woodstorks' fishing hole is just beyond a stretch of deeper water, but it's snake and alligator country, so keep your hands in the boat.'

Melanie jerked her hands from the canoe's sides to her lap instantly, her eyes wide and busily scanning the water as they approached the archway.

The moment they passed through, the sunlight speared painfully at her eyes, and she pulled her hat on and tied the scarf under her chin. Even under the shade of the brim, she blinked repeatedly while her eyes adjusted to the brightness of open water after the dim light in the forest.

They had emerged on to a highway of water that separated the mangroves from the waving plain of sawgrass on the other side. The canoe veered left with the current and floated leisurely southwards. Cage used his paddle primarily as a rudder, to keep the small aluminium craft in the centre of the slow but steadily moving stream.

They'd drifted perhaps a mile when a hammock of land with a single mangrove tree jutted out from the sawgrass on their right, constricting the water's flow.

With a startled lurch of her stomach, Melanie saw the now unmistakable lumpy forms of alligators sunning themselves on the tiny patch of dry ground the mangrove had gathered around its roots like a skirt. She went rigid on the seat, hoping they could slip by without disturbing them.

On the way around the hammock, the current slowed to a sluggish trickle, forming a stagnant pool of greenish slime that brought the canoe to a halt directly opposite the alligators' beach.

'Snake,' Cage hissed from behind her, pointing over her shoulder at a wedge-shaped head slicing through the scum on the water, an arm's length from the front of the canoe. 'Cottonmouth, no less. This place is full of them.'

Melanie shuddered as she watched the sinewy movements of the loathsome thing, seeing malevolence rather than grace.

'Can we get through here?' she whispered urgently over her shoulder, worried about a bank of reeds that seemed to block their progress forward.

'Sure we can, but not just yet.' Cage dipped the paddle and steered across the pond, towards the forest on the left. 'We'll beach the canoe and stretch our legs a bit first. The woodstorks fish in a shallow spot just beyond those reeds, and, if they don't show, the alligators should keep us entertained for a while.'

'And the snakes,' she grumbled.

'Those, too.' The canoe made a squishing sound as it bumped into the mush of submerged land at the edge of the forest. 'Jump out and tie us to that big root—the way I showed you, remember?'

Melanie hesitated. 'Are you sure it's solid? When we came through it back there the whole forest was under water...'

'It's dry here,' he said with a trace of impatience, struggling to hold the canoe steady. 'Look at the trees, the plants...oak doesn't thrive in standing water; neither does holly.'

Lips pinched tight, fighting the urge to snap at him that she wasn't any damn botanist so how was she supposed to know which plants were which and

whether or not they grew in water, she stood gingerly
in the wobbly canoe. With the rope in her hand and
her heart in her throat, she leapt to what she hoped
was dry land and nearly kissed the ground when it
didn't swallow her up. Moving rapidly so he wouldn't
see how badly her hands were shaking, she tied the
rope to a root the size of a man's waist. It irritated
her a little that the unsteady craft barely wobbled as
Cage stepped lithely from the back to the front, then
to the shore. He carried a bulging pack under one
arm. 'Lunch, such as it is,' he explained, walking
inland a few feet and brushing a tangle of damp leaves
from the base of a giant tree with his foot. 'Come on.
Sit down. We'll eat, drink, and watch alligators.'

She moved carefully towards him, testing the
ground with each foot before putting her weight on
it, finally sagging to lean against the trunk next to
him. 'I don't feel very safe here,' she confessed, her
eyes glued to the reptiles sunning on the other side of
the narrow strip of green water. About twenty
swimming strokes, she thought. That was all it would
take for her to cross that deadly pond. A 'gator could
probably do it in a single whip of its powerful tail.
She jumped when one of them bellowed and snapped
at a companion before settling back into a sunning
stupor.

'The alligators aren't a threat as long as we keep
our distance,' he said mildly, digging into the pack.
'Besides, the shore on this side is a little too sheer for
them to climb comfortably.'

She accepted a Thermos lid brimming with cool
juice and drank gratefully. 'What about the snakes?
The cottonmouth we saw? *He* probably wouldn't have
any trouble crawling up that bank, would he?'

He handed her a corncake with a guarded expression. 'Relax, Melanie. I checked for snakes before we sat down.' She blanched, remembering him kicking away the leaves. Somehow the idea that a snake might have been there was more than enough to terrify her. 'And if one happens to come along we just sit perfectly still until it passes...' He hesitated, and she knew he was thinking of yesterday. 'They don't *hunt* humans, you know. Not even the cottonmouth.'

She sat motionless, filled with a sudden, overwhelming hatred of snakes, alligators, heat, biting flies, juice in plastic Thermos lids... of the Everglades in general. She understood for the first time the pioneers' obsession to chop down the primeval forests and burn off the grasslands; to destroy the habitat of the things you feared, so you wouldn't have to be afraid any more.

'You're shaking.' Cage's voice was as gentle as his touch on her arm, but she still jumped.

'I want to get out of here,' she whispered, her lips barely moving. Her eyes were fixed and intensely blue, her pupils tiny, panicked pinpricks. 'I want to get back in the canoe and leave this place—now.'

'There's nothing to be afraid of...'

'Please. You don't understand. This is your world, not mine.'

'It isn't mine, either,' he said quietly, his eyes drifting to the green water where deadly snakes swam, to the hideous beasts lazing on the other side, up to where a lone hawk painted predatory circles across the blue canvas of the sky. 'It's theirs. At least, it was.' He looked back at her calmly. 'But we'll leave if you like. You can see as much from the canoe, I suppose. All the other tourists do.'

Even softly spoken, she heard the recrimination in his tone. He wanted her to see more than the tourists saw; to experience and at least respect, if not appreciate, the savage beauty of this place as he did; but she couldn't. Fear kept clouding all her senses. The small reserve of her new-found courage had already been drained by the choices she'd made in the last twenty-four hours. She just didn't have any left.

He started to get up, then stopped and looked at her. 'You hate everything about the Everglades, don't you?'

'I'm afraid of it.'

'And fear translates into hate. It always does. It's why our ancestors hated each other, with a few notable exceptions.' He tipped his head and sighed quietly. 'It's ironic, isn't it? If this place is going to survive it's going to need a champion, and the only one available happens to be a woman who hates it, a woman so timid that she's afraid to chart the course of her own life.'

Melanie straightened and felt the bark of the tree trunk scrape her back. 'Yesterday I would have deserved that,' she said carefully. 'But not today.'

The level of the contempt in his face hit her like a physical blow. 'You lost your virginity last night, not your timidity,' he said tonelessly, rising slowly to his feet, glancing over at where the canoe was tied.

His face didn't even change expression to give her a warning of what was to come. One second he was standing there; the next he was gone, leaping down to the bank with a shouted curse, jumping into the water's edge, clinging to a stationary root with one hand while his other arm stretched through the slimy water, reaching desperately for the white rope that drifted maddeningly just beyond his fingertips.

Her expression sick with disbelief, Melanie scrambled to her feet and stared at the canoe drifting aimlessly away from their shore, across the scummy pond towards the alligators' bank, the rope trailing behind on the surface like a leisurely white snake. She knew in an instant that it was too late, that the rope was already beyond Cage's reach; but for an agonising moment more he refused to admit defeat, his arm still stretching through the water, the cords in his neck taut and bulging with the effort.

Finally he pulled himself back on to the bank and stood with his shoulders slumped and his chin on his chest, breathing hard, water dripping from his soaked shirt and trousers to puddle at his feet. 'Damn,' he muttered under his breath.

For a moment Melanie just stood there, unable to speak, her lips folded in on themselves, her hands pressed flat against her chest. It was all her fault. They were stranded in this terrifying place, and it was all because she was so stupid, so helpless, so damned incompetent that she couldn't even tie a simple knot.

She steeled herself as he started to raise his head to look at her, prepared for the onslaught of his justifiable rage, but when their eyes met he just shook his head tiredly. Melanie burst immediately into tears.

'Oh, for heaven's sake,' he grumbled, moving quickly to take her into his arms, and she didn't know which was making her cry all the harder—that his arms were around her again, albeit reluctantly, or that he wasn't yelling at her as she deserved. She buried her face in her hands and sobbed against his chest while the wet from his clothes soaked into hers.

'It's ... all ... my fault. Dammit, I can't ... do anything right ...'

His hands moved awkwardly on her back, trying to soothe her. 'It wasn't your fault,' he said gruffly. 'It was mine. I should have checked the rope.'

It wasn't true, of course, and they both knew it. The words were simply the gift of a kind heart, and because kindness was one thing she hadn't seen in Cage, and was the last thing she expected in the circumstances, she sobbed harder still.

He stood like a rock, silent and comforting, just holding and stroking her for a very long time. The worst part of the whole incident was that once again Melanie found herself leaning on him, depending on him, and once again she was devastated by the realisation that this was where she wanted to be forever, and where she would probably never be again.

Sheer exhaustion finally quieted her sobs to an occasional, almost comical hiccup. She pushed away from his chest and wiped her eyes on her shirt-tail. 'What are we going to do now?' she sniffed miserably.

He lifted her chin with one finger and almost smiled at her. 'We'll improvise. If we can't manage to snag that rope we'll just find a way to the airboat through the woods, and come back for the canoe later.'

She looked out at where the canoe rested in the middle of the water, its rope still floating just a few inches too far from their shoreline. 'It sounds too simple.'

'Everything's simple, once you know your choices. Are you all right now?'

She sniffed and nodded, avoiding his eyes. 'Can we really get to the airboat through the woods?'

'Eventually. We'd have to do some pretty innovative trail-blazing, I'm afraid. It's only about two or three miles downstream, but there's a lot of marshland between here and there we'd have to find a way around. It could take most of the day.' He pursed his lips thoughtfully, looking out towards the canoe. 'Let's see what we've got to help us drag that damn thing back to shore.'

The pack yielded several packets of trail mix, sweets, a tightly coiled rope, a flashlight, and a snake-bite kit that made Melanie's eyes go wide. The very fact that he carried such a thing with him made the possibility of snake bite all too real.

'Ah. This is what we need,' he said, pulling a loop of broad elastic from the kit.

'What is it?'

'With a twist of a stick, it can be a tourniquet,' he replied absently, attaching the length of rope to the elastic circle. 'But maybe, with a little luck, I can use it to snag the cleat on the bow of the canoe.'

Melanie felt the first stirrings of hope and watched anxiously as he stood on the very edge of the bank, tossing the rope again and again towards the canoe. The slapping noise it made on the water disturbed the alligators on the opposite shore, and a few growled irritably and slid into the green depths. His best effort, with the line fully extended, fell a foot short.

'Dammit, it's so close...' he muttered, gazing around as if he expected to find a longer rope hanging from a nearby tree. His eyes finally came to rest on a broad, gnarled branch that jutted a few feet out over the water. 'There's the extra distance we need. I'll try from up there.'

Melanie felt the hollow leap of fear in her stomach. 'Don't climb out there...' she started to say, but he was already scrambling over the aerial roots of the old tree, straddling the branch, shinnying cautiously along its length until his feet dangled over the water. Like a cowboy astride a horse, he straightened, swung the makeshift lasso in larger and larger arcs at his side, then flung it towards the canoe.

Mouth open, heart in her throat, Melanie watched the elastic loop sail across the water, hesitate in mid-air as if it were weightless, then drop in a perfect circle over the cleat. 'You did it!' she cried, jumping up and down, clapping her hands in excitement, startling every alligator left on the shore into a frantic thrashing that sent sand flying in clouds around them.

The sound of the crash was sudden and heart-stopping, and, when Melanie jerked her head to look at where Cage had been, for a moment all her frantic thoughts could piece together was that somehow he had just disappeared into thin air. For an eternal second she remained frozen, her breath caught in her throat, then she saw the ragged wound where the branch had broken and raced over to find Cage's limp form half in, half out of the water, his head flung back on a rock-hard knot of the limb that had given way beneath him.

'Cage!' she screamed, crouching on the bank, reaching to grab under his arms before he could slide totally into the water, pulling with a strength she didn't know she had.

Blood rushed in her ears and her heart pounded against her rib-cage as she grunted and heaved and wept and cursed and, through some miracle, finally managed to drag him up on to the bank. Oblivious to the pain of pulled muscles in arms and shoulders and back, she hovered over him, whispering his name hysterically over and over again.

He looked almost peaceful, lying there with his eyes closed, his expression as serene as hers was twisted with terror; but there was a foreboding pallor beneath the bronzed skin of his face, and the flattened grass under his head began to turn red.

CHAPTER ELEVEN

NOTHING in Melanie's sheltered life had prepared her for what she faced now. In that first split-second when she saw the red stain spreading on the grass beneath Cage's head she felt her mind shatter like an exploding bomb, with a million pieces flying off in all directions, each piece representing a question there was no one there to answer. In their simplest form, they all boiled down to the biggest question of all, the one she felt like wailing to the emptiness around her. What am I going to *do*?

But that was in the first second. Before her racing heart had taken another beat she felt an extraordinary, totally unexpected wave of calm rise from somewhere deep inside. Within an instant her tears stopped, her pulse quieted, and her thoughts almost dazzled her with their clarity. She had to take care of Cage.

There was a visible pulse beating just beneath the line of his jaw. Encouraged by that, she began to explore the wet tangle of his hair, lifting his head ever so gently until her hand found the gash oozing blood. In seconds she had stripped down to her T-shirt and folded her overshirt into a thick, hard pillow of fabric she placed directly under the gash, hoping the weight of his head would create a crude pressure bandage. There was too much blood, she thought, terrified that the shirt wouldn't stop it, that he'd bleed to death while she watched . . .

Relax, relax, she commanded herself sternly. You aren't going to do him any good if you get hysterical now. Besides, didn't you read somewhere that even superficial head wounds bleed profusely? Just wait a minute; see if the bleeding slows down; and do what else you can in the meantime.

But what else was she supposed to do? Should she try to wake him up? What if he had a concussion? Didn't something terrible happen if you didn't wake concussion victims and keep them awake?

She bit down hard on her lower lip, racking her brain for the tiniest piece of buried information, feeling the thread of panic start to unravel again. She fought it with deep, hard breaths, clinging desperately to a thin edge of control.

Her eyes never left his face as she counted aloud to sixty with forced slowness, the terrified little girl inside hoping against all reason that he'd open his eyes and laugh at the way her voice was shaking; maybe pull her into his arms again and pat her back and tell her everything was going to be all right, not to worry, he'd take care of everything, just as someone had always taken care of everything for her.

By the time she got to sixty all those little-girl hopes for a last-minute reprieve had been dashed. Cage wasn't going to wake up and make everything all right. He was still lying there, deathly still, with only that tiny beat in his throat giving any promise of life at all.

She took a deep, shaky breath and eased his head up from the thick folds of her shirt, checked the wound, and thought the bleeding might have slowed. Next she ran her hands cautiously over his arms and legs, nearly sobbing with relief when she found no obvious broken bones.

'Cage.' Her hands braced on either side of him, she bent until her braid dangled on his chest. 'Benjamin Osceola Cage. Can you hear me?' She put her ear close to his mouth and held her breath, then tried again. 'Asi? Talk to me, Asi.'

The rasp of a grasshopper shattered the stillness, signal to all the creatures that had been frightened into silence when the branch broke. A red-winged blackbird trilled an answer from its wavering sawgrass perch; a small fish leaped from the water and came down with a splash of its tail; but Cage said nothing.

Still hovering over him, Melanie placed her hands on his cheeks, her lips folded in on one another. Even unconscious there was such pride in his face, such an aura of strength behind the sleeping features—but he was so pale beneath his tan now, so very pale.

Dammit, it just wasn't fair. This was all backwards and upside-down. The strong were always taking care of the weak—not the other way around. What kind of cruel, twisted fate would place the life of such a strong man in the hands of a stupid, helpless woman who couldn't even tie a simple knot?

She licked her lips, oddly dry in spite of the humidity, and looked down at the man who had broken her heart because he hadn't been able to love her. How pathetically unimportant that heartbreak seemed now. What did it matter that he couldn't return the love she felt? That didn't stop it from existing, and it didn't diminish her need to give it, either.

'I love you, Asi,' she murmured out loud, understanding for the first time what the words really meant. She'd always believed that love, like everything else in life, had to be an exercise in the art of give and take; but it wasn't like that at all. Giving was the important part—giving without reservation, without conviction, without promises and even without hope—that was love. The first Melanie Brooks had known that. It wasn't necessary for Cage to love her back to keep her love alive; it was only necessary that he continue to exist. For that, she was willing to give anything.

'I have to leave, Asi,' she said quietly. 'But I won't be gone long. Just stay here and rest, and before you know it I'll be back . . .'

She had to push herself to her feet with her hands, her legs were shaking so badly, and even once she'd managed to rise they nearly collapsed under her weight.

The trick is not to think about it, she told herself as she pulled off the heavy rubber boots and stripped out of her canvas trousers. Because if you let yourself think about it you're going to fall apart, and it's not like there's a line of stand-ins waiting to take your place.

She'd known the options the minute she'd seen the pallor of Cage's face. Even then, even before she'd finished hauling him up to the safety of the bank, she'd already made the only possible choice. What was it Cage had said? That everything was simple once you knew your choices? So she'd seen the choices, she'd picked one, and now she was going to act on it. Cage would be proud of her.

Overland through the forest, the airboat was hours away, if she was lucky enough to find it at all; but downstream, in the canoe, it was only a couple of miles. There really was no choice to be made, when you thought about it; just an unwavering certainty of what had to be done.

Clad in silly, lacy bikini panties and the awful mud-green T-shirt, Melanie paused on the edge of the bank and looked out at where the canoe floated, two ropes now trailing from its bow. It rested precisely halfway between her and the alligators. Ten strokes, she remembered as she stepped down into the water, the muddy bottom squishing between her toes; ten swimming strokes out, and ten back. That's all it will take. You're a good swimmer, a smooth swimmer; you can do that. Twenty strokes altogether. A child could do that.

The green scum lapped at her knees, then her thighs, then seeped into the brilliant white of her panties to stain them forever. She wasn't even looking at the water, because she knew if she did she'd see thousands of deadly cottonmouths and snapping turtles as big as she was and toothy alligators with hungry grins—whether they were there or not.

Instead she narrowed her vision to a single spot on the distant aluminum canoe where the sunlight reflected a metallic flash so bright that it nearly blinded her. Totally focused on that tiny square inch of brilliance, she took another step and felt the sucking pull of mud as the bottom reluctantly released her feet. The moment she felt herself suspended, supported by deep water, her arms started to move in slow, controlled strokes that barely rippled the surface.

She heard a faint splash to her right. Don't look! she told herself. Don't even think about it. Think about something else . . .

Reluctantly, her mind produced a vision of Cage on that first day, striding powerfully across the airfield towards her, eyes black and hot as boiling pitch, hair swept back from a lofty brow. Seven more strokes to go...

Something smooth and slithery brushed against her calf, then curled loosely around it, and she felt a jolt to her heart. Snake? Fish? Maybe just an underwater reed, it doesn't matter, as long as you don't think about it...they don't hunt humans, you know...but maybe you shouldn't kick your legs, just fight that instinct to kick as hard as you can and scream and only move your arms slowly, slowly, that's it, your legs will follow...

Whatever was down there slipped away as she moved forward through the water, trying not to think about the things that lurked in the depths of a greenish-black Everglades pond. Her lips pressed so tightly together that they hurt, she kept her eyes glued to that bright spot on the canoe, just five strokes away now, trying to call back an image of Cage's face— Asi's face—suspended over her in the golden light of late afternoon...

Her right hand sliced the air, tiny droplets catching the sun, then entered the water noiselessly directly on top of a thin, serpentine shape. She froze instantly, rounded eyes still fixed on the canoe just ahead, afraid to blink, afraid to look. The snake moved just a little under her hand and she swallowed a shrill scream of horror, then out of the corner of her eye she saw the white shape under her fingers. She had been so totally focused on the canoe, so intent on its being the ultimate goal, that she had forgotten the two white ropes that lay much closer. One of them now lay just under her hand.

Not a snake, not a snake, her mind babbled hysterically while her fingers closed around the rope and she started to turn back towards the shore. Halfway through her turn she caught a glimpse of movement from the opposite bank. Frozen by fear, she watched the alligator rise on its stubby legs and lift its pointed snout into the air. It was less than twenty feet away.

Oh, dear heaven, can it smell me? Can it hear me? Can it see me? her thoughts jittered frantically as she tried to tread water with as little motion as possible.

A brilliant, alien eye seemed to connect with hers across the water, reflecting, perhaps, on what she might taste like. The long toothy jaw opened, then clicked shut.

For the first time Melanie felt the chill of the water. It seeped through every pore into her bones. She wanted to finish her turn and race back to Cage, but her muscles wouldn't obey.

Move, dammit, move! her mind screamed inside her skull, but a force stronger than her fear kept her still, legs moving only enough to keep her afloat. The tension of waiting for the inevitable attack was so agonising that when the beast finally slid into the water she felt a perverse relief. At least she wouldn't have to wait any more. At least she wouldn't have to be afraid any more. In a minute it would all be over. Her eyes closed in a brief spasm of regret, then opened, as empty as the blue sky overhead.

With a gaze of dull resignation, she watched the alligator move towards her, wicked snout and bulging eyes barely visible above the surface. When it turned abruptly and headed downstream all she could do was blink in shock, barely able to register the reality of what had happened.

Her mouth sagged gradually in disbelief, her heart raced with renewed hope, and her eyes followed the alligator as his tail whipped him through the reed bank, into the clear water beyond. 'Thank you,' she whispered after him, as if the alligator had made her a conscious gift of her life. 'Thank you, thank you,' she kept repeating under her breath, over and over again, as she turned and swam woodenly back towards the bank. The canoe trailed obediently behind her, like a dog on a leash.

By the time she got back to Cage the gash in his head had stopped bleeding. As she knelt on the ground next to him, water still sheeting from her shivering body, she thought that his colour seemed better.

With the mechanical movements of an automaton she dressed as quickly as possible then started to lift Cage gently by the shoulders. She hadn't even stopped to consider the logistics of moving the dead weight of a strong, well-built man from the bank down to the waiting canoe, and in truth it never occurred to her that the feat might be beyond her. Whatever was left of her fading strength would be enough, simply because it had to be.

He stirred and groaned when she started to move him, and his eyes fluttered, then opened. 'Melanie? What the hell...?' He braced himself shakily on one forearm and reached for the back of his head. 'Hell, what happened?'

She caught his hand gently before he could disturb the wound, her own shaking so badly that it seemed a miracle she could control it at all. 'Don't touch it,' she warned him. 'You're hurt.'

'Tell me about it,' he said drily, his expression pained. 'I feel as if I just went ten rounds with a bull 'gator.'

She fought back the hysterical laughter bubbling in her throat, the tears rising in a tidal wave behind her eyes. 'The branch broke beneath you,' she told him in a choked voice, 'and you cracked your head. We have to get you to a hospital, Benjamin...'

'Hospital?' He scowled at her, but his eyes seemed a little unfocused. 'I don't need a hospital. What are you talking about...?' He wobbled a bit on his arm and she reached out to steady him.

'Easy...you've lost a lot of blood. Do you think you can stand? We have to get you into the canoe.'

'Hell, yes, I can stand,' he grumbled, but the short distance to the canoe turned out to be an exercise in endurance for both of them. Melanie saw the blood drain from his face as she helped him to his feet; heard his teeth grinding with effort as he tried to take his own weight.

'Dammit, Cage, lean on me,' she ordered him, wrapping both arms around his waist, bracing herself to take his weight.

'I thought you'd never ask.' What started as a grin ended in a grimace as he draped his arm heavily over her shoulders.

Getting him down from the bank and into the canoe was the worst part. Melanie grunted at the sharp, sickening pull of muscles stretched too far in her back and shoulders, but at last he was lying in the bottom of the canoe, facing Melanie on the stern seat. Paddle in one hand, her other on the rope that tied them to the root on the bank, she eyed his face worriedly. He seemed to be having trouble keeping his eyes open,

and she was afraid he would drift back into uncon-
sciousness at any moment.

'Cage. *Cage*. Don't fall asleep yet. Tell me how to
get to Everglades City.'

'Upstream... about five miles...' he grunted,
wincing. 'Or downstream... a mile past the
airboat... there's a ranger station...'

'All right,' she said quickly, leaning forward to
brush his cheek with her fingers. 'We'll go downstream. Rest now. No more talking.'

She untied the rope quickly and pushed away from
the bank with one hand. The canoe was halfway into
the middle of the pond before she'd worked out how
to steer with the paddle.

'Melanie?'

'Hmm?' Her lips were thinned in concentration as
she made the turn back out into the main stream of
the waterway.

'How did the canoe get back to shore?'

The fickle craft was veering too far to the right,
towards the sawgrass, and she had to paddle hard to
correct it. 'I went and got it,' she murmured
distractedly.

He was very quiet. Too quiet, and Melanie felt a
flutter of panic in her stomach. 'Asi?' she whispered,
jerking her eyes quickly to his face, the paddle suspended over the water in mid-stroke.

His eyes seemed more focused now, quietly intent.
'I'm still here, Melanie,' he said softly, looking at her.

She closed her eyes briefly in relief and kept
paddling.

CHAPTER TWELVE

THE doctor nudged Melanie's shoulder gently, waking her. She sprang to immediate attention in the vinyl waiting-room chair, wincing at a hundred dull pains coming from muscles all over her body. The grey-haired man in the white coat smiled sympathetically.

'You look worse than Benjamin,' he said, not unkindly. 'You sure I shouldn't be treating you instead?'

'How is he?' she asked breathlessly. 'Will he have to be flown to Miami?'

The park ranger, apparently a friend of Benjamin's and as concerned for his welfare as she was, had taken them by airboat to the closest clinic. It was staffed by the best, he assured her, equipped to handle anything short of major surgery, and, if Ben needed that, they'd airlift him to a Miami hospital.

'He'll be fine,' the doctor soothed her. 'Only took ten stitches to close that gash on his head, and the concussion is mild. We'll keep him here for a day or two, but the worst he'll be left with is a dandy headache for a week or so. Frankly, I'm more worried about you...'

'I'm fine,' Melanie insisted. 'Just tired.'

The doctor clucked his tongue sceptically and sighed. 'Well, get yourself home and to bed, then. You can see Benjamin tomorrow if you like. You have a ride?'

She nodded. 'The ranger that brought me here is waiting outside, down at the dock.' She hesitated, frowning hard. 'Doctor... the thing is, I'm leaving for Tallahassee early tomorrow morning...could you tell Benjamin...?' The words, whatever they might have been, wouldn't come. What could she say? She took a deep breath and forced a tremulous smile. 'Could you tell him goodbye for me?'

The doctor cocked his head and raised one bushy white brow. 'That's it? Just goodbye? From what he was babbling in there when I was sewing up his head, I thought...'

'Just goodbye,' she said hurriedly, pushing herself up from the chair, commanding legs wobbly from fatigue to carry her just a little further to the exit. At the last minute she turned and looked over her shoulder. 'Thank you, Doctor. Thank you for taking care of him.'

Just as she was about to push open the big glass doors to the outside, she caught a glimpse of her reflection and started. Lord, no wonder the ranger had looked at her askance when she'd first burst into the station. No wonder the doctor had looked at her the same way, convinced she had to be sick to look *that* bad.

Her braid was a tangled mess; the T-shirt and canvas trousers were filthy, and where her skin wasn't smudged with mud it was coated with a dried film of green from the pond. 'Behold the flower of Southern womanhood,' she said wryly at her reflection, then she pushed the door wide and walked out into the muggy Florida evening.

The ranger's name was Tom, and a relieved smile split his freckled, sunburned face when she told him that Cage was going to be all right. 'Take more than a little bump on the head to put old Ben out of commission for long,' he said brusquely, but his voice gave away just how worried he'd been. He took her back to the park station by boat, then on to Cage's cabin by Jeep. Melanie had slept for most of the trip. 'You sure you want to stay here alone tonight?' he asked, looking doubtfully out of his window at the dark cabin. 'I could run you up to one of the motels...'

Melanie wanted to throw her arms around him and give him a grateful kiss, but she decided that, the way she looked and smelled, it might be more of a kindness not to. 'I'm sure.' She managed a warm smile and squeezed his hand. 'You could do me another favour, though, if you're going to see Benjamin.'

'Sure I will. Thought I'd stop by the clinic tomorrow and see how he's doing.'

'Would you tell him I borrowed his Jeep to get to the airstrip? I have an early flight out tomorrow.'

'No problem. I'll pick him up when Doc says he can go home, and we'll collect the Jeep then. Park it on the north side of that big tin pole building. That's where Ben always leaves it when he flies out.'

She nodded, peered once more at the darkness outside, then took a breath and climbed out of the Jeep. She closed the door, then bent to say a last goodbye through the side-window. 'Thanks again, Tom. For everything.'

'Here, Melanie. You take this with you.' He handed her a heavy metal flashlight. 'You'll need that to find the oil lamps, let alone light them.' He gave her a two-fingered salute just before pulling away. 'You take care, now. Hope to see you again soon.'

She watched his headlights bounce and flutter through the black forest until she couldn't see them any more. After a time the cicadas and frogs restarted the night symphony interrupted by the noise of the Jeep. Melanie stood there for a while, listening, soothed by the sounds of nature's syncopation. Eventually her lips curved slowly into a smile, because she was all alone in a totally dark wilderness, and she wasn't afraid.

Beau was waiting on the tarmac when the little charter plane taxied to a halt the next morning. He looked crisp and elegant in a light linen suit, his omnipresent grin a white slash through the perfect tan of his face. Melanie saw him first from the plane window and wondered how he could look exactly the same when things were so different. She felt as if she was looking at someone she'd known only in passing, a very long time ago.

And I was going to marry him, she thought numbly. I would have married him, borne his children, and spent the rest of my life believing that was the way things were supposed to be. She shivered a little, chilled by the thought, and looked down at the thin booklet resting on her lap—a booklet that had taught her as much about Beauregard Parker as it had about the impact of the water-management system on the Everglades.

At the hiss of compressed air that announced the plane door's opening, she sighed heavily and rose to her feet, handbag clutched in one hand, the booklet in the other. She wondered if Cage would mind that she'd taken it from the cabin; if he'd approve of what she intended to do with it.

Aside from a slight sunburn she'd concealed under a dusting of powder, she looked exactly like the woman who had boarded this very plane just a few days before. Her navy suit with the white piping was classically elegant; her freshly washed hair gleamed on her shoulders in honey-blonde waves; and her blue eyes were as wide and bright as ever. But that was just the package, just the superficial window-dressing. She wondered if Beau would be able to see through that, to know immediately that the woman inside was very, very different.

'Mellie! Darling!'

He stood at the bottom of the short flight of aluminum steps, grinning up at her as she made the descent. A ripple of flashes from behind the terminal gate captured the moment. Melanie glanced over and saw the tight cluster of media people waiting, and felt her stomach roll.

'Hello, Beau.' She winced at the force of his closed, dry lips on hers.

'Mellie, darlin', are you ever a sight for sore eyes,' he drawled into her ear, wrapping her in an embrace that set off another round of camera flashes in the distance. 'Don't pay any attention to them,' he whispered, directing a dynamite smile towards the very people he was telling her to ignore. 'We'll dodge a few questions, then get out of here.'

'They'll want to know what I learned on my trip, Beau.'

'And I'll tell them, darlin', at my Press conference tomorrow. Don't you bother your pretty little head about it. Just tell them you had a nice time, honey.'

Gritting her teeth against his blatant condescension, wondering if he'd always treated her this way and she just hadn't noticed or minded, Melanie allowed herself to be led towards the mob of waiting reporters. Strobe lights clicked on as the video cameras whirred to life, and half a dozen voices called out half a dozen questions all at once. Most of the questions were frivolous—had she seen an alligator? Had she ridden in an airboat?—and for a moment she despaired that she would even have a chance to deliver the little speech she'd prepared; then one voice sang out louder than the rest.

'Did Benjamin Cage present any real evidence that this budget cut would do irreparable harm to the Everglades?'

She turned towards the voice and looked into the serious dark eyes of the man who owned it. Knowing that her reply would change her life forever, she hesitated for a moment. 'As a matter of fact,' she finally managed to reply, 'he presented some very convincing evidence indeed.'

There was immediate, total silence, perhaps because the reporters were surprised to hear her speak at all. It was obvious, Melanie thought ruefully, that they weren't nearly as surprised as Beau. She felt his fingers tighten convulsively on her shoulder, and his entire body went rigid next to her. A glance at his face showed that even his smile seemed frozen.

Thinking that swimming in snake- and alligator-infested waters was a lot less dangerous than this, she cleared her throat nervously. 'Some of you may not realise that southern Florida's fresh water supply is entirely dependent on the Everglades,' she began softly. 'I know I didn't. I didn't know that the Everglades made its own rain; that it acts like a giant filter, cleaning the water that fills our wells. And I didn't know that we were destroying that filter by draining too much land—did you?' She paused and looked over the audience, into each set of eyes that would meet hers. 'Billions of gallons a day are diverted to irrigate the huge corporate farms to the north, and the chemical run-off from those farms is killing the Everglades, acre by acre. We have to stop them.' She heard Beau's sharp intake of breath next to her, and went on quickly, her words coming so fast that they almost ran together. 'If we don't stop them we won't just be destroying the Everglades; we'll be destroying our own supply of fresh water. It's all in here.'

She held up the booklet, turning to give every camera a full shot. She heard the steady whirr of the video cameras, the distant rumble of a small jet coming in for a landing, but other than that there was utter silence. 'I'm certain that once Congressman Parker has read this study,' she added, 'he'll want every one of you to read it, too.'

The silence stretched for another interminable moment, then, as if responding to some unseen, unheard signal, the crowd came to immediate, noisy life. The air was pummelled with a dozen different questions, shouted all at once. Where could reporters get a copy of the study? Why hadn't it been released to the public? What did Beau intend to do with this new information?

Beau's smile wavered as he blinked uncertainly, holding a hand palm-out as if to deflect the clamour. 'That's all for now, folks. Miss Brooks needs to rest after her tiring trip. Excuse us, excuse us...' He smiled good-naturedly, guiding Melanie through the crowd, his hand uncharacteristically tight on her upper arm as he steered her expertly to a waiting limousine and slid into the plush interior beside her. 'Miss Brooks's hotel,' he told the driver, still waving at the Press through the side-window.

Once the big car was on the highway, he pushed savagely at the button that closed the privacy window behind the driver and turned sideways on the seat to face her. His face was incredibly red, and Melanie noticed the cords standing out on the side of his neck. 'Where the *hell* did you get a copy of that report?' he snapped at her.

Melanie stared at him, a little saddened by her first look at the man who had been hiding beneath that glorious smile and those courtly manners all along. 'Cage gave it to me . . . or, rather, I took it. I told him I was sure you hadn't seen it, but you have, haven't you, Beau? You've read it already.' It wasn't really a question.

'Yes, I've read it! And it's garbage!' He snatched the booklet from her hand and flung it across the seat.

She folded her hands in her lap, noticing that her fingers felt strangely cold. 'Then you know that there's a list in there of all the men who own those corporate farms—the ones killing the Everglades.' Her expression was as flat as her tone. 'They were all at our engagement party, Beau. Every one of them. They were the men who financed your campaign; the men who paid to get you elected. And, in exchange, you agreed to fight for this budget cut, didn't you? To make sure there wouldn't be money for any more research studies like this one; to make sure no one ever found out that the life was being drained from the Everglades to line the pockets of a few very rich men.'

Something shifted under the handsome, aristocratic features; something hard and unpleasant and ugly. 'Don't meddle in things you don't understand,' he said evenly, his gaze frighteningly cold. 'I don't know what happened to you down in that God-forsaken swamp, but whatever it was apparently made you forget your place. I'm not going to have any wife of mine speaking her mind in front of the media the way you did back there, and——'

'I liked speaking my mind, Beau,' she interrupted with a strange smile. 'I didn't think I would, but I did, and who knows? I just may do a whole lot more of it in the future.'

'Not as *my* wife, you won't...'

It was the smile that disconcerted him most. 'No, not as your wife,' she agreed.

A short time later the limousine pulled up in front of Melanie's hotel. Nothing further had been said between them, but somehow they both understood that there was nothing more to say. As passionless in death as it had been in life, their relationship simply fizzled.

Ever the gentleman, Beau walked around the outside of the car to open her door personally. While she waited Melanie took the copy of the study from where it had fallen between the seats and slipped it into her bag.

By sunset that evening, every television and newspaper reporter in the city of Tallahassee had a copy of their own, covered with a note that said simply, 'Courtesy of Melanie Annabelle Brooks.' She signed each note personally with a grand flourish; proud, at last, of her own name.

CHAPTER THIRTEEN

THAT night the local television stations and newspapers all did lengthy reports on the newly discovered study of the Everglades water-management system. Watching the coverage on her hotel-room television, Melanie saw the film of her speech at the airport again and again. Ironically, Congressman Beauregard Parker was credited for bringing this critical information to the public's attention, and reporters praised him lavishly for 'sending his own fiancée to ferret out information others had tried to suppress'.

Melanie shuddered to see how adroitly Beau donned the sudden, undeserved mantle of hero when he found himself in the rather awkward position of receiving accolades for the very act he had tried to prevent. Yes, he told one reporter, the corporate farms attacked in the study had indeed been large contributors to his campaign; and yes, he was certainly going to lose their support after making the study public; but he'd felt a moral imperative to sacrifice his own career, if necessary, to bring the voters the truth.

She rolled her eyes at that and turned off the set.

Part of her wanted to expose Beau for the deceptive, self-serving creature he really was; but for the moment she just didn't have the stomach for it. Perhaps some day she'd have the strength to speak out against Beau, and politicians like him; hell, maybe some day she'd really get involved in politics and run for public office herself; but not just yet. It was all

she could do now to get from moment to moment
without stumbling over her own pain.

Anticipating the luxury of a long soak, she slipped
into a tub filled with fragrant, bubbly water. The
moment she leaned back and closed her eyes she saw
Cage's bronzed face, eyes dark and blistering, sunlight glancing off the sharp line of those exotic cheekbones. She sat up quickly, sloshing water over the rim,
suddenly deciding that a shower would be better than
a bath anyway. With the last of the bubbles swirling
around the drain and hot water beating on her
shoulders, she imagined she saw the flicker of a
dragonfly's wings in the spray sheeting off her body.
'Oh, damn,' she murmured softly, covering her face
with her hands, closing her eyes—but then she saw
Cage's face again on the insides of her eyelids, the
dark eyes softer and deeper now, haunting her. As if
she could escape the image inside her head, she backed
into the wet tile wall, then slid down to sit on the hard
porcelain, hugging her knees, letting the water pummel
her body for a very long time.

Much, much later, with the world outside her
window shimmering with that first hesitant glow of
pre-dawn, she huddled on her bed and placed a call
to the clinic. Mr Cage was resting comfortably, a
sleepy night nurse told her. Any message?

Melanie hung up and fell back on to a pile of
pillows, seeing a wavering image of a broad back in
a black T-shirt walking away. She didn't know if her
eyes were open or closed.

She was ready to leave Tallahassee by sunset of the
next day. She'd woken deep into the afternoon, groggy
and exhausted, her eyes swollen from crying in her
sleep. After forcing down a room-service luncheon

plate, she packed with a kind of frenzied care, concentrating furiously on stupid little things, like the way she folded her clothes, to keep the aching emptiness at bay. She had no master plan, no foreseeable purpose for her life, only a driving need to leave this city and all the memories it held of the woman she used to be. An image of the family mansion in Creek County wavered in the fog of her thoughts like a secret haven seen through a spring mist, but it wasn't where she wanted to be—it was just the only place she had to go.

At last she was standing over her suitcase on the bed, ready to close and snap the lid. In it were all the clothes Cage had bought her at Hildy's store, washed, pressed, and neatly folded by the hotel's laundry.

She smiled ruefully at the crease they'd ironed into the ugly canvas trousers; at the rounded toes of the ungainly rubber boots poking out from beneath them. She wondered what her own descendants would think when they found these things in the next century, carefully, lovingly stored in the family attic.

Her fingers trailed lightly over the shirt top—the one she'd worn the last day—then started when she caught a glimpse of herself in the dresser mirror across the room. She'd packed every item of clothing she'd brought, completely forgetting that all she was wearing was the peach and blue robe she'd worn at Cage's cabin.

With a forced, wry smile at her own absent-mindedness, she stripped down to her underwear, then dressed in the canvas trousers and one of the bulky overshirts. It didn't matter what she wore for travelling. She'd rented a car for the drive up to Georgia, and no one would see her anyway. Come to think of

it, it didn't matter if she *was* seen. She stared at her
reflection as she pulled her long blonde hair back into
a pony-tail, thinking that she liked the way she looked
in these clothes. They reminded her of who she really
was; they reminded her of three precious days she
would hold in a cherished part of her memory forever.
Maybe she'd never take them off.

She closed the suitcase and called down for a
bellman to come to collect her bags.

A few moments later he banged on the door, so
hard that it made her jump. Up until now the em-
ployees of the hotel had been so deferential that it
had almost bordered on the absurd, but this sounded
as if the bellman had actually used the side of his fist
on the door. Irritated, she hurried to jerk it open. The
sharp reprimand she intended to deliver died on her
lips.

Cage stood painfully erect in the doorway, backlit
by the golden glow of the hallway lights. He wore a
starkly white dress shirt open at the collar and a pair
of snug, faded jeans, as if he'd started to dress for-
mally and had changed his mind at the last moment.

A single band of white gauze rode just over his black
brows, circling his forehead. The black hair was
ruffled by wind and finger tracks, and a few strands
spilled over the white gauze strip. His eyes were dark
and hot and steady.

Melanie blinked once, hard, as if she didn't trust
the evidence of her eyes. 'You're at the clinic,' she
said foolishly. 'You're supposed to be there for
another day or two at least. Why did they release you?'

'They didn't.'

'But . . .'

'I saw you on television. They keep replaying that little speech you gave at the airport.'

She stared at him mindlessly, lips slightly parted, blue gaze wide and unblinking.

'You threw it all away, Melanie.'

Her pale brows twitched in confusion and her head tipped until her pony-tail dangled off to one side.

'Beau,' he explained. 'Your marriage; the life you'd planned . . . everything. You threw it all away.'

Melanie's brow cleared. 'Oh. That.'

He almost smiled. 'Yes. *That*.'

Peripherally Melanie saw the uniformed figure of the bellman appear behind Cage, but she never took her eyes from his, nor he from hers.

'Your bags, miss?' the bellman asked politely.

'Later,' Cage growled without turning his head, and the man disappeared. Cage continued looking at her for a moment longer, then sighed. 'You might as well ask me in, Melanie. I'm not leaving until I say what I came here to say.'

She glanced down at where her hand still clung tightly to the doorknob, as if that were all that was holding her upright. She knew what was coming. He'd come all the way up here to thank her for what she'd done for his Everglades, and, although his motives were noble enough, she didn't know if she could bear it.

What was she supposed to do? Smile graciously while he told her what a fine thing she'd done? Stand within touching distance of a man who would forever be out of reach, and pretend it didn't matter? Wouldn't it be easier to ask him to leave; to never, ever have to look on his face again and feel that agonising pain around her heart?

'Melanie?'

'Come in,' she mumbled, standing aside, closing her eyes as he walked by into the room, feeling the slight movement of the air he displaced like a hurricane-force wind against her body.

Oh, lord, she thought, maybe I can get a job in his orange groves or his factory, so that once in a great while he might walk past me on his way to somewhere else, and I can feel the air that touched him touching me. That would be enough, wouldn't it? That would be enough to make life worth living . . .

'Come here, Melanie.'

Her eyes flew open and she turned her head to look at him. He was already over by the easy chairs in the sitting-room, and here she was still standing by the door, holding it open as if she expected someone else to walk in. She licked her lips, swallowed, then released her death grip on the door. It swung closed with a quiet click, and she moved woodenly to within a few feet of him.

His eyes swept over her as she approached, brows twitching at the bulky shirt and comically creased canvas trousers. 'You're leaving Tallahassee?'

She gripped the back of a chair and wondered if she looked normal; if it only felt as if she was falling apart at the seams. 'Yes. I'm going back home. Back to Creek County.'

Just like my great-great-great-grandmother, she added to herself. We Brooks women just keep going around and around that same circle, never really closing it, and we all end up back in Creek County.

He nodded once, then turned to look out the picture window. It was almost full dark now, and the lights of the cityscape stitched a random pattern of sparks across the black void beyond the glass. Melanie's gaze shifted to the thick bandage on the back of his head, held in place by the gauze band.

'How's your head, Benjamin?' she asked quietly.

'My head's fine.'

She frowned at the sudden chill in his voice. 'You shouldn't have left the clinic...'

The impact of his eyes almost pushed her backwards. 'And you shouldn't have jumped into that pond!' The sheer volume of his shout was like a hard slap across her face. 'You could have died in that water! Why the hell did you do that? Why the hell didn't you go overland to the ranger station? Why the *hell* didn't you just wait until I——?'

'Because!' she shouted back helplessly, because shouting was the only way she could keep from bursting into tears. 'Because you were hurt! Because I thought you were...' her voice broke and she had to swallow hard before continuing '...I thought you were dying.'

His head jerked convulsively, sending his hair flying across his brow. 'Dammit, what if *you* had died? Did you think I'd want to live in a world without you?'

Melanie felt the breath stop in her throat like a wad of dry cotton; felt every muscle in her body freeze. She was afraid to move, afraid to speak, afraid that even a breath might shatter this single bright bubble of hope that had suddenly, magically appeared.

He was facing her like a coiled beast caught in a trap, eyes narrowed, shoulders hunched, fists clenched at his sides. 'I didn't want to love you.' His voice crackled deeply, and Melanie felt its electricity shooting through the nerves of her body like a live current. 'I didn't ever want to love a woman so much that my life would be over if she left . . .' his gaze grew distant and he looked past her, back in time '. . . and then I saw you get off that plane and I knew that you were the woman I would love like that, and I also knew that you could never belong to me; that eventually you would leave.' He shoved his hands in his pockets, looked at the floor, then up into her eyes with a sad little smile. 'And, even knowing all that, I couldn't help myself. I tried telling you love was the one thing I couldn't give you, but the truth was, I'd already given it by then. The morning after we made love I was crazy enough to hope you'd say you wanted to stay—it nearly killed me when you didn't.'

Melanie took the quick, desperate breath of a drowning person who suddenly, miraculously found her head above water in the clean, sweet air. Her heart took a giant leap in her chest and she opened her mouth to speak, but he shook his head.

'You don't have to say anything. I knew from the start we were as different as two people could be; as star-crossed as our ancestors. I was just part of your first adventure, that's all.' He tipped his head with a self-deprecating smile. 'It's funny, isn't it? You were supposed to be one of those old-fashioned, helpless, dependent Southern ladies; but, underneath, you were the strong one—strong enough to throw away your future to do what you thought was right; strong enough to risk your life to save someone else's . . .' He took a breath, then straightened to deliver the highest accolade Melanie would ever receive in her life. 'She'd be proud of you, you know. The first Melanie Annabelle Brooks would be so proud that you carry her name.'

She was so stunned by the wonder of the things he was saying that her lips seemed frozen in place. Besides, even if she could speak, what would she say? How could she twist and compress the things she was feeling into something as pathetic as mere words? What did you say when someone reached across the vacuum of your existence and handed you love, handed you the reason for being...?

'Cage!' He had crossed the room and his hand was on the doorknob before she finally found her voice. 'I'll find out where you live,' she said in a choked voice, and then she almost laughed out loud, because she was hopelessly in love with this man and didn't even know his address. 'If you walk out that door, I'll find you somehow. If I have to I'll camp out in that cabin of yours and just wait until you come back.'

His hand still frozen on the knob, he turned his head slowly to look at her. She couldn't read whatever lay behind his eyes, not from this distance; but she didn't have to. She already knew what was in his mind and his heart and his spirit; she felt as if she'd known it for a hundred years.

'What?' he asked softly.

'I'll find you,' she promised, her voice stronger now, but tears were streaming unchecked down her cheeks. Benjamin gazed at them in wonder. 'I'll find you because I *am* an old-fashioned Southern lady; the kind who wants to be married, to have children playing in her attic, and... oh, Asi... I want them to be yours.'

He took a few steps towards her, then hesitated, and for the first time she saw naked emotion in that proud, stoic face, the tortured expression of a man afraid to believe what he most wanted to believe; afraid to love because love was the only thing that

could hurt him. And then she saw a strange sort of
peace settle on his face, and knew that he had cast
the fear aside.

He stood motionless, gazing at her across the short
distance that separated them, as if he would never
again have a chance to see her from this far away.
Melanie felt as if she was being drawn into those black
eyes; being *absorbed* by them, committed to a memory
that would endure long past the short span of one
man's lifetime.

'We'll have your portrait done,' he murmured, 'just
the way you look now, and we'll hang it next to hers,
where our grandchildren can always see them . . .' He
paused and smiled crookedly at the baggy trousers
and shirt. 'Why are you wearing those clothes,
Melanie?'

She smiled through her tears. 'I love these clothes.
I might never take them off.'

His eyes touched hers, a new light shining from their
depths. 'Want to bet?'

Melanie felt her chest rise beneath her shirt, felt her
heart rise beneath her breast, and imagined she heard
the fluttery thunder of a thousand birds taking flight.
She lifted her right arm as he lifted his left, and with
the profound silence of love too old, too great to be
spoken aloud, their fingers touched like phantom tendrils of history linking one century to another.

'I love you, Asi,' Melanie sighed as he pulled her
into his arms, not quite sure if she had spoken or only
merely thought the phrase. Ear pressed to his chest,
she heard the rapid thunder of his heart like an Indian
drum.

Outside, from a seemingly cloudless, starry night,
a gentle, smiling rain began to fall as the sky wept.

Next Month's Romances

Each month you can choose from a wide variety of romance with Mills & Boon. Below are the new titles to look out for next month, why not ask either Mills & Boon Reader Service or your Newsagent to reserve you a copy of the titles you want to buy — just tick the titles you would like and either post to Reader Service or take it to any Newsagent and ask them to order your books.

Please save me the following titles:	Please tick	√
BREAKING POINT	Emma Darcy	
SUCH DARK MAGIC	Robyn Donald	
AFTER THE BALL	Catherine George	
TWO-TIMING MAN	Roberta Leigh	
HOST OF RICHES	Elizabeth Power	
MASK OF DECEPTION	Sara Wood	
A SOLITARY HEART	Amanda Carpenter	
AFTER THE FIRE	Kay Gregory	
BITTERSWEET YESTERDAYS	Kate Proctor	
YESTERDAY'S PASSION	Catherine O'Connor	
NIGHT OF THE SCORPION	Rosemary Carter	
NO ESCAPING LOVE	Sharon Kendrick	
OUTBACK LEGACY	Elizabeth Duke	
RANSACKED HEART	Jayne Bauling	
STORMY REUNION	Sandra K. Rhoades	
A POINT OF PRIDE	Liz Fielding	

If you would like to order these books in addition to your regular subscription from Mills & Boon Reader Service please send £1.70 per title to: Mills & Boon Reader Service, P.O. Box 236, Croydon, Surrey, CR9 3RU, quote your Subscriber No:......................................
(If applicable) and complete the name and address details below. Alternatively, these books are available from many local Newsagents including W.H.Smith, J.Menzies, Martins and other paperback stockists from 12th March 1993.

Name:..

Address:..

....Post Code:...........................

To Retailer: If you would like to stock M&B books please contact your regular book/magazine wholesaler for details.

You may be mailed with offers from other reputable companies as a result of this application.
If you would rather not take advantage of these opportunities please tick box ☐

Another Face . . .
Another Identity . . .
Another Chance . . .

When her teenage love turns to hate, Geraldine Frances vows to even the score. After arranging her own "death", she embarks on a dramatic transformation emerging as *Silver,* a hauntingly beautiful and mysterious woman few men would be able to resist.

With a new face and a new identity, she is now ready to destroy the man responsible for her tragic past.

Silver – a life ruled by one all-consuming passion, is Penny Jordan at her very best.

W●RLDWIDE

4 FREE

Romances
and 2 FREE gifts
just for you!

You can enjoy all the
heartwarming emotion of true love for FREE!
Discover the heartbreak and the happiness, the emotion and
the tenderness of the modern relationships in
Mills & Boon Romances.

We'll send you 4 captivating Romances as a special offer from
Mills & Boon Reader Service, along with the chance to have
6 Romances delivered to your door each month.

Claim your FREE books and gifts overleaf...

An irresistible offer from Mills & Boon

Here's a personal invitation from Mills & Boon Reader Service, to become a regular reader of Romances. To welcome you, we'd like you to have 4 books, a CUDDLY TEDDY and a special MYSTERY GIFT absolutely FREE.

Then you could look forward each month to receiving 6 brand new Romances, delivered to your door, postage and packing free! Plus our free Newsletter featuring author news, competitions, special offers and much more.

This invitation comes with no strings attached. You may cancel or suspend your subscription at any time, and still keep your free books and gifts.

It's so easy. Send no money now. Simply fill in the coupon below and post it to -
Reader Service, FREEPOST, PO Box 236, Croydon, Surrey CR9 9EL.

- - - - - - - - - - - - - NO STAMP REQUIRED - - - - - - - - - - - - -

Free Books Coupon

Yes! Please rush me 4 free Romances and 2 free gifts!
Please also reserve me a Reader Service subscription. If I decide to subscribe I can look forward to receiving 6 brand new Romances each month for just £10.20, postage and packing free. If I choose not to subscribe I shall write to you within 10 days - I can keep the books and gifts whatever I decide. I may cancel or suspend my subscription at any time. I am over 18 years of age.

Ms/Mrs/Miss/Mr_____ EP31R

Address_____

_____

Postcode_____Signature_____

Offer expires 31st May 1993. The right is reserved to refuse an application and change the terms of this offer. Readers overseas and in Eire please send for details. Southern Africa write to Book Services International Ltd, P.O. Box 42654, Craighall, Transvaal 2024. You may be mailed with offers from other reputable companies as a result of this application.

If you would prefer not to share in this opportunity, please tick box ☐